MYplace

FOR BIBLE STUDY

Published by First Place for Health
Galveston, Texas, USA
www.firstplaceforhealth.com
Printed in the USA

ISBN: 978-1-942425-42-7

CONTENTS

MY PLACE FOR BIBLE STUDY
Strength Will Rise

FOREWORD

I was introduced to First Place for Health in 1993 by my mother-in-law, who had great concern for the welfare of her grandchildren. I was overweight and overwrought! God used that first Bible study to start me on my journey to health, wellness, and a life of balance.

Our desire at First Place for Health is for you to begin that same journey. We want you to experience the freedom that comes from an intimate relationship with Jesus Christ and witness His love for you through reading your Bible and through prayer. To this end, we have designed each day's study (which will take about fifteen to twenty minutes to complete) to help you discover the deep truths of the Bible. Also included is a weekly Bible memory verse to help you hide God's Word in your heart. As you start focusing on these truths, God will begin a great work in you.

At the beginning of Jesus' ministry, when He was teaching from the book of Isaiah, He said to the people, "The Spirit of the Lord is on me, because he has anointed me to preach good news to the poor. He has sent me to proclaim freedom for the prisoners and recovery of sight for the blind, to release the oppressed, to proclaim the year of the Lord's favor" (Luke 4:18–19). Jesus came to set us free—whether that is from the chains of compulsivity, addiction, gluttony, overeating, under eating, or just plain unbelief. It is our prayer that He will bring freedom to your heart so you may experience abundant life.

God bless you as you begin this journey toward a life of liberty.

Vicki Heath, First Place for Health National Director

ABOUT THE AUTHOR

Karen Porter is an international speaker, a successful businesswoman, and the award-winning author of seven books including, "If You Give A Girl A Giant" and "Amplify!"

She is a frequent guest on regional and national radio and television programs, also writing a regular leadership column for *Leading Hearts Magazine* and contributing to various *Guideposts* publications. She has written for national magazines such as *Focus on the Family, Discipleship Journal*, and *American Taste*, and has written curriculum for Lifeway Christian Resources.

President of the Advanced Writers and Speakers Association, Karen serves on several boards, including First Place for Health. She is a certified coach for aspiring writers and speakers. She and her husband, George, own Bold Vision Books, a traditional Christian publishing company, as well as Stone Oak Publishing and kae Creative Solutions.

Karen served as vice president of international marketing for a major food company in Texas for more than 30 years. She traveled around the world, and her varied experiences (including dinners with Fidel Castro) contribute to the richness and depth of her writing and speaking.

Karen is a people-person, plain and simple, and you will love to laugh with her and maybe even cry a little as she shares her joys and struggles. She says her marriage to George is her greatest achievement, but she'd love to talk to you about her five grandchildren. In her spare time, Karen continues a lifelong quest to find the perfect purse.

ABOUT THE CONTRIBUTOR

Lisa Lewis, who provided the menus and recipes in this study, is the author of *Healthy Happy Cooking*. Lisa's cooking skills have been a part of First Place for Health wellness weeks and other events for many years. She provided recipes for seventeen of the First Place for Health Bible studies and is a contributing author in *Better Together* and *Healthy Holiday Living*. She partners with community networks, including the Real Food Project, to bring healthy cooking classes to underserved areas. She is dedicated to bringing people together around the dinner table with healthy, delicious meals that are easy to prepare. Lisa lives in Galveston and is married to John. They have three children: Tal, Hunter, and Harper. Visit www. healthyhappycook.com for more delicious inspiration.

INTRODUCTION

First Place for Health is a Christ-centered health program that emphasizes balance in the physical, mental, emotional, and spiritual areas of life. The First Place for Health program is meant to be a daily process. As we learn to keep Christ first in our lives, we will find that He is the One who satisfies our hunger and our every need.

This Bible study is designed to be used in conjunction with the First Place for Health program but can be beneficial for anyone interested in obtaining a balanced lifestyle. The Bible study has been created in a seven-day format, with the last two days reserved for reflection on the material studied. Keep in mind that the ultimate goal of studying the Bible is not only for knowledge but also for application and a changed life. Don't feel anxious if you can't seem to find the correct answer. Many times, the Word will speak differently to different people, depending on where they are in their walk with God and the season of life they are experiencing. Be prepared to discuss with your fellow First Place for Health members what you learned that week through your study.

There are some additional components included with this study that will be helpful as you pursue the goal of giving Christ first place in every area of your life:

○ **Leader Discussion Guide:** This discussion guide is provided to help the First Place for Health leader guide a group through this Bible study. It includes ideas for facilitating a First Place for Health class discussion for each week of the Bible study.

○ **Jump Start Recipes:** There are seven days of recipes--breakfast, lunch and dinner-- to get you started.

○ **Steps for Spiritual Growth:** This section will provide you with some basic tips for how to memorize Scripture and make it a part of your life, establish a quiet time with God each day, and share your faith with others..

○ **First Place for Health Member Survey:** Fill this out and bring it to your first meeting. This information will help your leader know your interests and talents.

○ **Personal Weight and Measurement Record:** Use this form to keep a record of your weight loss. Record any loss or gain on the chart after the weigh-in at each week's meeting.

○ **Weekly Prayer Partner Forms:** Fill out this form before class and place it into a basket during the class meeting. After class, you will draw out a prayer request form, and this will be your prayer partner for the week. Try to call or email the person sometime before the next class meeting to encourage that person.

○ **100-Mile Club:** A worthy goal we encourage is for you to complete 100 miles of exercise during your twelve weeks in First Place for Health. There are many activities listed on pages 265-266 that count toward your goal of 100 miles and a handy tracker to track your miles.

○ **Live It Trackers:** Your Live It Tracker is to be completed at home and turned in to your leader at your weekly First Place for Health meeting. The Tracker is designed to help you practice mindfulness and stay accountable with regard to your eating and exercise habits.

WEEK ONE: STRENGTH WILL RISE BECAUSE ... I DECIDE

SCRIPTURE MEMORY VERSE

He has saved us and called us to a holy life — not because of anything we have done but because of His own purpose and grace. This grace was given us in Christ Jesus before the beginning of time... 2 Timothy 1:9

Our road to strength begins with an Old Testament passage from Joshua — the story of how Israel crossed into Canaan (the Promised Land) and claimed the promises of God. You may think the Old Testament is difficult to understand, but the Apostle Paul said the story of the nation of Israel is an example for us.

> *For everything that was written in the past was written to teach us, so that through the endurance taught in the Scriptures and the encouragement they provide we might have hope.* **Romans 15:4**

Many of us like to travel, taking excursions to new and interesting places. An island experience, a cruise aboard a luxury liner, a mountain expedition, exploring a city, or a peaceful rest near a lake. We usually come home to our same life and routine with photos and memories to remind us of the trip. But what if a trip changed your life forever? What if what you saw and felt caused big changes in your life at home?

In the next weeks, we will follow Israel's journey as they crossed the Red Sea and the Jordan River and moved into the new life God promised them. They were forever changed. As we follow them, we will also take a trip into the full life God has promised us.

We will be changed in two ways. First, by Scripture, which is our example, our guide, and life to our souls. Perhaps this familiar verse about the Word will give new insight if we read it from The Passion Translation: "For we have the living Word of God, which is full of energy, and it pierces more sharply than a two-mouthed sword. It will even penetrate to the very core of our being where soul and spirit, bone and marrow meet! It interprets and reveals the true thoughts and secret motives of our hearts" (Hebrews 4:12, TPT). As we study the Bible, we will be changed forever.

The second life-change is because First Place for Health is part of our journey from unhealthy habits and conditions to life, health, happiness, and purpose. The program of First Place for Health transforms us if we commit to living healthy in all four areas of our lives: spiritual, physical, mental, and emotional.

Jesus said, "The thief comes only to steal and kill and destroy; I have come that they may have life, and have it to the full" (John 10:10). That full life is a life of peace, hope, contentment, joy, and freedom. And victory.

—— DAY 1: CROSSING THE RED SEA

Lord, we believe You loved us long before we loved You. Thank You for Your salvation — the gift to us that cost You everything — the shed blood of Your Son.

"Let's start at the very beginning; a very good place to start." This famous line made memorable by Julie Andrews in the movie, "The Sound of Music," rings a sweet melody in my mind when I look back at life and see the experiences that shaped who I am. Today we are going to remember our most important day — the day we crossed the Red Sea.

At the end of the Book of Genesis, Jacob's family moved to Egypt because one of his sons, Joseph, held a high position in the Egyptian government — he was second in command of the entire country. Read Genesis 46:26-29. Where did the family settle, and how many were in the family?

_____

_____

They lived in Egypt about 400 years and grew to be a large nation. Describe what happened to them when new leaders came to power. Exodus 1:8-11.

_____

_____

How did the people of Israel react to hard labor as slaves? Exodus 1:12-13; 3:9

_____

_____

What did God do? Exodus 3:10.

_____

_____

After a series of horrible plagues and Moses' continued negotiation, Pharaoh agreed to let the people go. Where did they camp? Exodus 14:1-2.

_____

_____

According to researchers, Migdol wasn't a city; it was a military outpost. Imagine how the Egyptians must have wondered about this huge group (some scholars count them in the multiple millions) setting up camp between the military outpost and the Red Sea. The officers used carrier pigeons to report what they saw; they flew five hours to get back to the palace headquarters. When Pharaoh heard the news that the people were trapped at the Red Sea, he regretted his decision to let them go. He mustered his army and all his chariots and charged toward the sea to bring his slaves back.

As he approached, God walled up the waters of the sea, and the nation crossed over on dry land. The Egyptians chased close behind, but God let the wall of water go. Pharaoh and all his army were drowned. Israel was rescued.

When the Israelites crossed the sea, they were rescued out of slavery and bondage. Dramatic. Spectacular. Life-giving.

I believe each person must cross the Red Sea in a definitive moment of salvation — a specific time when we decide individually to believe in and follow Christ. It's a personal decision — not that we're a Christian because our family was Christian, or that we joined a group of people who were Christian, but when each of us personally decides Jesus is our Savior.

Read Acts 16:30-31. What is required of you to you accept Jesus as Savior?

_____

_____

_____

Read 1 John 1:9. What does God do when you turn to Him, asking for forgiveness?

_____

_____

_____

Read Ephesians 2:8-9. How does Paul describe salvation?

_____

_____

According to John 8:32, what gives us freedom?

_____

_____

My Red Sea moment happened in Texas when I was 11 and my family attended the national camp of our church denomination. One afternoon a little girl drowned; a sad and horrific tragedy. That night during the evening worship service my mother asked, "Karen, if that had been you who drowned this afternoon, where would you be right now?" I knew I had no claim on Heaven, and because I'd been in church all my life, I knew what I needed to do. I knelt on the concrete floor and prayed, "Jesus, I have sinned, and I accept Your gift of forgiveness. I trust You to save me." My memory of that moment is clear and powerful. I felt a sweet cleansing and immense peace. Throughout my life, if I have any doubts about my relationship with God, I go back in my mind to that spot on the second row of that rustic tabernacle, and I remember my glorious salvation. It was the night I crossed the Red Sea — rescued from the bondage and slavery of sin.

Think about your Red Sea moment. When did you ask Jesus to save you? Where were you, and what was the situation? Describe what happened.

_____

_____

If you have no memory of a moment when you personally decided to follow Jesus, accepting His mercy and grace and payment for your sins, please talk to your First Place for Health leader. He or she will be delighted to show you the road to salvation. If you'd like to talk to anyone on the First Place staff about it, never hesitate to contact us.

Your salvation experience is pivotal for your life. Trusting Christ for salvation opens the door to joy and integrity. Knowing Him helps you love others and love yourself enough to start the journey to health and wellness. Strength rises because He walks with you as you eat and exercise. He becomes your partner in all areas of your life: spiritual, physical, mental, and emotional.

Lord, You rescued a huge nation by Your power over nature. You rescued me from the punishment for my sin when You gave Your life on the cross. Thank You for Your gift of salvation. Thank You that Your love for us is so strong.

—— DAY 2: CROSSING THE JORDAN RIVER
Lord, thank You for allowing me to cross over from death to life in salvation. Now help me live life to the fullest.

Imagine trying to walk into a dense stand of trees where the underbrush is so thick you can see only a few inches ahead. In your imagination, see the vines and branches and old logs lying on the ground, and feel the spiderwebs as you try to make your way through the woods.

Now imagine a wide-open space with beautiful vistas; see a clear path through lovely flowers blooming in all colors.

One is a vision of chaos and restriction with not much potential, the other a panorama of possibilities, opportunities, and promise. Today we will see how God takes the tangled mess of our lives and gives us purpose, peace, health, wellness, and joy. When we are rescued and saved (our Red Sea), we become recipients of all God has promised. Read John 10:10. What did Jesus say?

_____

_____

_____

Yet many of us are not living in abundance because we have stayed stuck in a pattern of shallow spirituality. Since the journey of the nation of Israel is a pattern for us (Romans 15:4), we should learn from the mistakes of this people and emulate their successes.

Read Joshua 1:11. Where did the Israelites go after they crossed the Red Sea?

_____

_____

_____

For 40 years the nation wandered from the Red Sea in a desert wilderness. Then they ended up at the Jordan River ready to go into the land God had promised them. In the coming weeks, we will discover some valuable lessons from their time in the wilderness — but today let's jump forward to the day they crossed the Jordan River.

Read Joshua 3:5-8. List some interesting facts you discovered.

_____

_____

_____

We learned yesterday that the Red Sea experience is an example of our salvation — that moment when we trusted Jesus, Who rescued us from slavery to sin. What do you think the Jordan River represents in our spiritual life? Read Hebrews 6:1, Colossians 2:6-7, and 1 Peter 2:2-3 to help you.

_____

_____

After we experience salvation (our Red Sea moment), each Christian needs another crossing — this time from living in a shallow spiritual way to living in a new reality of being totally sold out to God and totally dependent on Him. Just as the Promised Land was called "a land of milk and honey" (Exodus 3:8), Jesus has promised us an abundant life of joy, peace, purpose, and fulfillment. Theologically, the Red Sea represents salvation and the Jordan River represents the beginning of our sanctification (read more in Appendix A).

I've met some people whose trip from the Red Sea to the Jordan River was short. Almost from the moment they accepted Christ, they began to live fully and completely for Him. This kind of quick journey often happens to those who become believers as adults — discovering the peace of Jesus is so dramatic, they begin their new life immediately.

I've met others who took a long journey after salvation and struggled in the wilderness. Perhaps they were saved when they were young, yet made some bad choices along the way and ended up in addictive situations or followed other sinful patterns. After years of trouble, setbacks, and painful living, they returned to the Lord and began serving Him. Sometimes these wilderness journeys last for many years.

The journey doesn't always look like a wilderness, but it also may not be the abundant life Jesus promised. My story is a bit like that. After I accepted Jesus, I learned about my religion and the rules of my family and church. I lived by those rules and tried to serve God by doing good works and having perfect church attendance. I worked hard and somehow in my head, I equated filling iced-tea glasses at church suppers with being sold out to Jesus.

The wilderness where spiritual growth takes place is not necessarily barren. It will be helpful for us to think about our spiritual journey after we crossed the Red Sea and recognize it as a wilderness experience. But first, let's look at a few examples of spiritual growth.

****

When a Pharisee named Saul met Jesus on the road to Damascus, Jesus changed his name to Paul, and the man was transformed by the power of salvation. His life changed from persecuting Christians to being a leader of Christians — and writing most of the New Testament. Before Paul ventured into his new ministry he spent three years in Arabia and Damascus (Galatians 1:15-24). Some scholars describe these years as Paul's process of getting ready for the great ministry that lay ahead. Perhaps he spent much time in prayer and studying Scripture so he could present the great doctrines of the New Testament.

Think about the writings of Paul and copy your favorite verse below. What does it mean to you? (If you don't have a favorite Paul verse consider one of mine: Galatians 5:24, Ephesians 6:10, Philippians 3:8, Colossians 3:10)

_____

_____

_____

****

The prophet Jonah didn't want to preach in Nineveh because he hated the Ninevites for their cruelty and paganism. He didn't want God to be merciful. He tried to run away and ended up inside a great fish, which was a kind of wilderness for him.

Read Jonah 2:2-9 and describe what you think he learned.

_____

_____

_____

****

Abraham and Sarah received a remarkable promise from God: they would be the parents of nations. Yet Sarah had never been pregnant with even one child. The two waited a lifetime until they were in their 90s, as God continued to give Abraham the promise. Once during those years, he and Sarah acted in disobedience and tried to produce an heir with a surrogate mother (Genesis 16). Waiting for the promise to come true was a wilderness for Abraham and Sarah.

Waiting can feel like a wasteland for many of us. When have you waited for the Lord to answer your prayers? What did you learn from that time?

_____

_____

_____

What is your spiritual story from the moment you accepted Jesus as Savior to the time you realized God had more abundance for you?

_____

_____

_____

The Jordan River represents crossing out of the wilderness into the Promised Land. What did Jesus say in John 6:35 and 8:12 about living the promised abundant life?

_____

_____

_____

Read Deuteronomy 20:4, and Psalm 31:19 and 55:22. What are the spiritual characteristics of living to the full?

_____

_____

_____

How does the First Place for Health program help you live life to the full?

_____
_____
_____

What are some wilderness traps that keep you from living fully?

_____
_____
_____

Spiritually

_____
_____
_____

Physically

_____
_____
_____

Mentally

_____
_____
_____

Emotionally

_____
_____
_____

Read Proverbs 3:5-6. How do we pass into the deep and rich life Jesus promises?

_____
_____
_____

Lord, my desire is to be more like You. I understand sanctification is a process. Please lead me on the path toward holiness, and to the richness of Your will. Help me follow You across the Jordan River into the abundant life You promised.

—— DAY 3: DECIDING TO FOLLOW

Lord, my heart is full of desire to follow You. I want to live the abundant life You prom-
ised. Please remove all my hesitation and reluctance, and give me grace to follow You
completely.

Wouldn't it be great if we could make all our decisions by a coin-toss? What to wear — heads, the blue shirt; tails, the green shirt. Where to go — heads, the movie; tails, the circus. Life is full of decisions: what college to attend, which house to buy, what job, which restaurant, what activity, what friend, and on and on. Scientists say there is a difference in deciding something that plays it safe like a guaranteed $10 bill vs. choosing a risky investment for a potentially higher payoff. Research shows that taking a risk becomes easier if we see someone else take that risk and succeed. Researchers concluded that if you want to find purpose and happiness and success, you don't have to decide which restaurant to go to or which food you will order. Instead, ask this question: "With whom will I go to the restaurant?"

Your first and biggest decision is who you will spend time with. When you surround yourself with people who have attitudes and behaviors you desire, you will succeed. For example, choose friends who exercise more, watch less TV, or take up a musical instrument, and your decisions will be better. The people you hang out with have an impact on your decisions and behaviors (weforum.org: "A neuroscientist who studies decision-making reveals the most important choice you can make").

Let's search Scripture to see some of what God says about making decisions.

Read Deuteronomy 6:5. What is our best choice about love?

_____

_____

_____

Read Deuteronomy 30:19-20. What is the choice in this verse? How does verse 20 say we can make the choice?

_____

_____

_____

What choice must each person make, according to Romans 10:9 and Revelation 3:20?

_____

_____

_____

What attitude should we choose as we live our lives, according to Colossians 3:17?

_____

_____

_____

How should we choose to live, according to Mark 8:34, Hebrews 11:6, and Psalm 119:30?

_____

_____

_____

You have chosen to be in a First Place for Health group. List some of the healthy traits and characteristics you observe in other members.

_____

_____

_____

What decisions will you make about your health because of what you see?

_____

_____

_____

One weekend evening I attended a marriage-vow renewal ceremony on the beach. It was beautiful and fun, then the couple treated the guests to dinner in a lovely nearby restaurant. The celebration and collection of friends was warm and inviting — and I made some poor food choices ending with a beautiful presentation of Bananas Foster. After I returned home, I started a downhill journey of overeating — warm, creamy pastries for breakfast, chips and creamy dip for a snack, thick juicy hamburger and fries for lunch, and by supper time, I was miserable. Not only had I binged on unhealthy foods, I was angry with myself for the choices I had made. It took me days to get back on track.

A few weeks later we took our beautiful granddaughter, who loves healthy food, to a nice restaurant. I chose a dish from the "skinnylicious" menu, and said no to the creamy cheesecake. After I got home, I felt freedom and satisfaction, first because I didn't feel bloated or too full, and second, because I knew I had made good choices. We can learn so much about decisions from these two examples.

What do you think caused me to make poor choices at the first restaurant, and what would have helped me?

_____

_____

_____

What do you think caused me to make better choices at the meal with my grand-daughter, and how do you think I can continue to make those kinds of choices?

_____

_____

_____

Choices do not define us. A poor choice does not make me a bad person, nor does a better choice make me a good person. God loves me when I choose well and when I don't. However, our choices (whether food or behavior) matter when we are trying to honor and obey the Lord.

Choices and decisions come in large and small packages. We make small choices every day — healthy or junk food, work or play, doubt or faith, joy or victim hood. Some decisions are big such as changing careers, retirement, or financial invest-ments. Even making no choice is a decision.

How does a decision or choice honor God? First, cover it in prayer. Second, search for answers in the Word of God. Third, confirm the decision with wise people. Three simple steps:

Pray for wisdom
Know the facts
Get good advice

In your First Place for Health journey, you will make big and small decisions about your wellness. A small decision to eat low-fat yogurt instead of ice cream or to take a walk when you'd like to sit on the couch. A large decision of commitment to the First Place lifestyle for a lifetime.

According to these verses, how can you become a great decision-maker?

_____

_____

_____

Matthew 6:10 _____

James 1:5 _____

James 3:17 _____

Dear Lord, we make so many decisions every day — from what job to take to what kind of coffee to order; from what stock to invest in to what to eat for dinner. We make decisions deliberately, consciously — and automatically and unconsciously. Father, help us face our decisions with courage and help us stop agonizing over these choices, because our faith in You is strong.

—— DAY 4: GETTING YOUR FEET WET
Lord, I have decided to follow You. I've made up my mind to go with You. Now, Lord, I beg You to help me take the first steps into the Promised Land.

Our family loves to ski. In fact, our children told us when they were young that if they had to decide between summer and winter vacations, they would always choose winter skiing. One year I had a terrible accident on top of Crested Butte in Colorado, when my skis caught an ice patch and I tumbled and rolled down the mountain. When I finally came to a stop, it was clear that my twisted leg was broken. After a long recovery, I was strong enough to get on skis again. But as I got off the lift high atop a mountain, fear gripped me. I couldn't find the courage to point my skis downward. To my family's embarrassment, I sat and scooted down the first slope. When I reached the next plateau, I faced my moment of truth. *Would I bow to my fear and slide down the mountain on my backside and never again experience the joy of swooshing through the trees with the wind and snow blowing through my hair?* I wanted to ski again; I had dressed in ski-clothes and taken the lift to the top, but now I had to take action. I stood up on my skis and went down the mountain, squealing with delight — joy is the result of overcoming fear, and defeating panic requires us to make a first step.

Crossing the Jordan River into our blessed, abundant life with the Lord begins with the decision we talked about yesterday — but once we decide, we must get our feet wet by taking action.

Read Joshua 3:2-3. What instructions did Joshua's officers give the people?

_____

_____

_____

Read Joshua 3:8. What did the priests have to do first?

_____

_____

God rarely shows us the whole picture. He asks us to take a few steps first, then He will open the way to the next few steps. As humans, we would much prefer to see the future and know how every situation will turn out. God asks us to trust Him for the next step. Some have described it as "just enough light for the step I'm on." As soon as I take that step, there is enough light for the next step. Some writers have compared not knowing the future to the way a car's headlights shine only a few feet ahead on a dark night. We can't see the curves and bumps in the distance; we can only see where the lights shine.

Imagine the priests carrying the Ark of the Covenant that day. The Jordan River was swollen out of its banks, so not only was it deep, but trying to walk across would have been difficult through submerged underbrush and weeds. One wrong step and they could be swept away by the current. It took courage and obedience and trust to take that first step — to be willing to get their feet wet.

Read Joshua 3:15-17. What happened as soon as their feet touched the water?

_____

_____

_____

The river was a barrier between the wilderness and the land God had promised — the border between their old life of wandering aimlessly and their new life of abundance and rest. Here is my paraphrase of how teacher and speaker Wayne Stiles explains that crossing the Jordan was a spiritual experience:

The priests went first. Not the warriors who might've made the people feel protected from potential enemies. Not the engineers who might've built a bridge or found the safest pathway. Not the adventurers or the younger crowd or the elders. Not even the best swimmers. The move across the Jordan was a spiritual move — the priests went first.

The trip across the river was a holy moment of transition for the Israelites. Transitions are a vital part of our Christian walk and in our First Place journey to physical, mental, emotional, and spiritual health. Do you have a raging river to cross? God will lead you through it, so do not retreat. Do not quit. Do not try to go around. He will take you through. Set your foot into the muddy water and see what God will do.

Throughout the Bible, the Jordan River is a place of transition.

Read 2 Kings 2:7-15. Describe how the river was part of the transition from the ministry of the Prophet Elijah to the younger Elisha. What did Elisha ask for and receive?

_____

_____

Read John 1:23, 26, 29-34. Describe the transition that happened when John baptized Jesus.

_____

_____

_____

The Jordan River is a place of transition. We face transitions in all areas of our lives — especially our health journey. When did you take the first steps to "get your feet wet" by changing your eating and exercise habits? What action did you take? What has worked for you and what hasn't?

_____

_____

_____

How did Joshua explain the significance of the Jordan River crossing in Joshua 3:10-13?

_____

_____

_____

How do these words encourage your First Place journey?

_____

_____

Lord, I don't always like or appreciate the transition moments of life. Help me see the value of change so clearly that I will take action in all four areas — Physically: eating food that is good for my health and moving my body to make it strong. Mentally: opening my mind to the power of learning. Emotionally: trusting You, not my feelings. Spiritually: reading and meditating on Your Word.

—— DAY 5: LEAVING THE WAY OF REBELLION

Lord, please remove thoughts of rebellion from my mind. Stop rebellious words from leaving my mouth. Curb my rebellious cravings and help me focus on obedience. Grow the fruit of the Spirit in me.

My family tells the story of one day when I was about two years old. My mom had given me an orange to eat, and, as you can imagine, I succeeded in getting the stickiness all over my face and hands. Armed with a wet washcloth, mom attempted to clean me up. Apparently, I fought the process and screamed that I'd do it myself. If you've ever heard a two-year-old say, "Me, me, me" or "Mine, mine, mine" or "Me do it." you can picture the scene. I dropped the washcloth and refused to pick it up. That's when daddy decided to enforce some discipline.

Several hours later, even with my parents' pleas and demands and eventual ultimatums — and a few well-placed swats to the top of my toes — nothing would convince me to pick up the cloth. Mother went to another room to sob; my big brother begged to pick it up; and daddy realized he'd gotten himself into an unwinnable battle of the wills with a rebellious two-year-old. All four of us were in tears and exhausted.

Sometimes being a rebel is good. When everyone else is going the wrong way, a rebel chooses the right course instead. Friends are drinking and doing drugs, yet the rebel refuses. The crowd's mindset is, "Do your own thing," but the rebel sticks up for what he or she knows is right. Or, to quote my mother, "When everyone else jumps off the cliff, don't you jump too." We laugh, but living a Christian life in our society may require us to rebel against certain attitudes and expectations.

But some rebellion is negative and not healthy. It can start when we are annoyed at an authority, and grow into outrage and refusal to obey. Many of us went through a rebellious phase in our teens, but some people flagrantly violate rules and social norms even as adults. Researchers say they 1) look for the thrill first, 2) crave attention — good or bad, 3) question everything, and 4) will try anything once.

Having a negative, rebellious spirit damages our relationships and is an affront to God. Look at the characteristics of a rebellious spirit below. Put a check by those that describe someone you know. Put an X by the ones that describe you. Some will have both a check and an X.

_____ _____ Puts his or her spin on the rules
_____ _____ Never listens to the rules
_____ _____ Deliberately argues the opposite view
_____ _____ Says whatever comes to mind
_____ _____ Doesn't care what others think
_____ _____ Wears wild or outrageous styles just for effect
_____ _____ Eats whatever he or she wants instead of what is healthy

Let's examine the rebellious spirit the nation of Israel carried into the wilderness. What happened when the people grew hungry? Read Exodus 16:2.

_____

_____

_____

When Moses went up the mountain to receive the Ten Commandments from God, what did the people do? Read Exodus 32:1.

_____

_____

_____

When the nation reached the edge of the Promised Land, they convinced Moses to send spies to report back about conditions there. The spies came back with a good report, saying, "It is a good land that the LORD our God is giving us" (Deuteronomy 1:25).

Read Deuteronomy 1:26-46. How did the people feel about the report? (vs. 32) What happened because of their rebellion? (vs. 35)

_____

_____

_____

After 40 years of wandering in the desert, the Israelites came again to the Jordan River and another opportunity to cross into the Promised Land. Moses had died, and Joshua was the new leader. God gave him a promise in Joshua 1:6-9. Paraphrase it here.

_____

_____

_____

Joshua sent messengers throughout the camp telling the people to get ready because the Lord was now going to lead them to their new home.

Read Joshua 1:16-18. How did the people respond? What stands out?

_____

_____

The difference between the two events is striking. In the first, the Israelites did not trust the report, nor did they trust God. Rebellion. In the second, they chose to believe and obey and follow God into the abundant life He had promised.

As you consider your life, how have distrust, disobedience, and rebellion played a role in your health choices?

_____

_____

_____

In your First Place for Health quest for health and wellness, how has a rebellious spirit hampered your progress?

Physical _____

Mental _____

Spiritual _____

Emotional _____

Now consider how trust, obedience, and submission changed your health choices in each of the four.

Physical _____

Mental _____
Spiritual_____
Emotional _____

Lord, when I follow You, I have a choice. I can return to the way of slavery, fear, and rebellion; or I can trust You with my future health and wellbeing. Lord, I choose trusting You.

—— DAY 6: REFLECTION AND APPLICATION
Lord, thank You for Your plan of redemption, and for coming to Earth to rescue us as our Savior.

HE HAS SAVE US
Our memory verse this week begins with the declaration, "He has saved us." This encapsulates the lessons we learned about the Red Sea and the Jordan River, and decisions we make or do not make.

Describe how you feel about your Red Sea moment, including any questions.
_____
_____
_____

Reflect about how each of the following verses reassures you.

"Very truly I tell you, whoever hears my word and believes him who sent me has eternal life and will not be judged but has crossed over from death to life" (John 5:24).
"Not everyone who says to me, 'Lord, Lord,' will enter the kingdom of heaven, but only the one who does the will of my Father who is in heaven" (Matthew 7:21).
"I write these things to you who believe in the name of the Son of God so that you may know that you have eternal life" (1 John 5:13).
"Therefore, there is now no condemnation for those who are in Christ Jesus … " (Romans 8:1).

Lord, You are the definition of love and You loved us first, even while we were sinners. Please give us the grace to show our love to You.

—— DAY 7: REFLECTION AND APPLICATION

Lord, You are Creator and Sustainer of the Universe. We are amazed that You care for us and that You have called us to a purpose greater than ourselves.

HE HAS CALLED US

The second part of our memory verse tells us why God rescued us and promised abundant life: "He has called us — not because of anything we have done but because of his own purpose and grace."

Read and meditate on the following verses.

"To this you were called, because Christ suffered for you, leaving you an example, that you should follow in his steps" (1 Peter 2:21).

"But just as he who called you is holy, so be holy in all you do; for it is written: 'Be holy, because I am holy' (1 Peter 1:15-16).

Listen for God's still, small voice and write what you believe to be His purpose for you.

_____

_____

_____

_____

_____

_____

Spend the rest of today praising and thanking God for His mercy and grace and purpose.

Lord, I praise You for Your plan for me. You have saved me, and You have called me, and You cover me with mercy and grace.

WEEK TWO: STRENGTH WILL RISE BECAUSE ... I SUFFER

SCRIPTURE MEMORY VERSE
My flesh and my heart may fail, but God is the strength of my heart and my portion forever. Psalm 73:26

We've looked at the miraculous Red Sea and Jordan River crossings. We've seen how God rescued the slaves from the bondage of Egypt, and how He opened the door to the new land promised to be filled with milk and honey. But a thorough examination of Israel's journey reveals there was a 40-year gap between the two crossings. During this time, the people of Israel wandered in the wilderness.

This week we will try to understand this journey. When we ask questions like, "Why did they wander?" or "Why did they suffer?" we often are asking about our lives, too. What could be God's reasoning when He allows suffering? Failure, accidents, sickness, loss, pain, separation, penitentiaries, hospitals, mental illness, death, murder, rape, pandemics, and so much more, cause deep suffering in our lives. If God is good, then why?

There are some answers in the Bible, and some answers may never be known until we reach Heaven; but no matter the suffering or pain, we know a few truths about God.

> *The LORD is gracious and righteous; our God is full of compassion. Psalm 116:5*
> *Where is another God like you, who pardons the guilt of the remnant, overlooking the sins of his special people? You will not stay angry with your people forever, because you delight in showing unfailing love. Once again you will have compassion on us. Micah 7:18-19a, NLT*

> *But the plans of the LORD stand firm forever, the purposes of his heart through all generations. Psalm 33:11*

The wilderness — and the suffering it brings — is part of God's plan. It's not easy to accept that statement when our pain is great. Even our journey to wellness is full of twists and turns and painful moments. When we've worked so hard to lose weight, yet it creeps up again sooner than we dreamed possible. Or we injure ourselves and can't move as freely as we would like. It's not easy to feel pain in our spirits or our bodies and we ask, "Why? Lord, why?"

This week we will dig deep to try to understand God's mindset and purpose for suffering, and we will remember Who He is and that He has always been faithful.

—— DAY 1: SUFFERING: AN UNEXPECTED REASON

Lord, it is difficult to understand Your purpose when I face suffering. I want to rejoice, but sorrow, grief, anguish, and distress overwhelm me. I ask for spiritual insight as You give me a glimpse of Your vision and reveal Your heart.

If God is love, why do people suffer, and how can a good God allow pain and misery? The questions aren't light, and they're not philosophical or theological — they're personal. Deeply personal.

In the Bible, one man suffered tremendously. His name was Job. We've heard about Job's patience, but I believe there is deeper meaning and richer understanding.

Read Job 1:1-5 and write what you learned.

Where did he live? _____
What kind of life did he lead? _____
What did you learn about his family and wealth? _____
_____
What did you learn about his spiritual life? _____
_____

Job was not sinless, but he was a man of integrity, without hypocrisy or duplicity. Job 1:6-12 records a conversation in Heaven when God and Satan discussed Job's blameless life. Satan strutted around the throne room bragging that Job's faith was commercial (he only loves you because you bless him — my paraphrase). Though Satan has access to the throne, he is not co-equal with God. He is not ruling from Hell as John Milton describes in "Paradise Lost." He will be cast into the fire as shown in Revelation 20:1-3. But today he roams the Earth.

On that day in Heaven's court, Satan asked God's permission to test Job. When God allowed it, the worst started happening. Job's family was killed and his fortune decimated. He didn't know his situation was a result of the accusations in the heavenlies, but Job 1:20-22 tells us he tore his robe in grief. What declaration did he make in the midst of pain?

_____

_____

_____

Charles Swindoll once said, "There are no U-Hauls behind a hearse." What does 1 Timothy 6:7 say?

_____

_____

_____

Job refused to give up faith in God or his integrity no matter what happened. Still, Job didn't understand why.

There are some difficult-to-see clues in the description of the scene in Heaven's court. Let's discover them together. Read Job 1:6-19 and write them here.

Clue 1: Who is in charge of the throne room? (vs. 6)

_____

Clue 2: Who did God offer as Exhibit One of a fine man? (vs. 8)

_____

Clue 3: Why did Satan say Job was so good? (vv. 9-10)

_____

Clue 4: What challenge did Satan give God? (vs. 11)

_____

Clue 5: Did God say the test was about patience? What does it seem to be about?

_____

What was Job's response? (1:20-22)

_____

_____

_____

Our worst can become our best. I lost my job, and we lost everything — house, money, jobs, savings, pride, identity. Yet I can say that it was the best thing that ever happened to me. The worst may be the best. I am closer to God and more dependent on Him than at any other time in my life.

Job didn't understand why he suffered, and we may never understand either. But because the Bible shows us what happened in Heaven's throne room, we can understand the why of Job's troubles: God used him as a weapon to defeat the devil. Satan thought Job would curse God, but Job instead trusted God. And because of his faith, Job became a tool — a weapon — in God's hand to defeat and silence the devil.

Job's pain was not a test — that's what Satan thought. His misery was not a punishment — that's what his friends thought. His faith deflated Satan's braggadocio and defeated his evil plans. You and I can defeat the enemy this way too. We are weapons used by God.

Read Ephesians 6:10-11 and 2 Thessalonians 3:3. How does God help us be powerful weapons against the Enemy?

_____

_____

_____

My wellness and weight and energy are a testimony to the world of God's goodness, and show how He can use an ordinary person like me. Being overweight and lethargic is not a good witness to the power and love of God. With His help, I can become a weapon to defeat the Enemy's evil plans against me.

Lord, I may not know the why of my situation until I get to Heaven, but I will walk by faith, not to endure or not to be proclaimed as patient; instead, Lord, use me as a weapon to defeat and silence Satan. I commit to live in faith, purity, integrity, and trust like Job so I will be a powerful deterrent to evil in this world.

—— DAY 2: SUFFERING: GOD'S MYSTERIOUS WAYS
Lord, suffering is difficult, especially when I can't see the future. Comfort me. Reassure me. Show me how Your ways are high above anything I can think or imagine.

Yesterday we learned that our suffering might be one of the weapons God uses to defeat Satan. When the Enemy says our faith is commercial or weak, God sees us as a prime example of faith and purity. The Enemy strikes and we trust God — and the Enemy is defeated.

There is another aspect of suffering we need to understand because sometimes our troubles and trials are part of being a Christ-follower, and how we respond may show the world the glory of God.

Read 1 Peter 4:12-13. What should our response be to suffering and why?

_____

_____

_____

What comfort did Jesus give about suffering in John 16:33?

_____

_____

_____

Let's consider how Jesus is our perfect example of the downward spiral of suffering. Read Philippians 2:5-8 and describe the steps Jesus took from Heaven to the cross.

Step 1: (vs. 6) He did not consider equality with God to be used to His advantage

Step 2: (vs. 7) _____

Step 3: (vs. 8a) _____

Step 4: (vs. 8b) _____

He loves us so much, He left the glory and power and perfection of Heaven so we could be rescued from sin and slavery to sin. Jesus' perfect life and innocent blood are the sacrifice required for salvation. If we compare the sacrificial steps required to live in health to the downward steps of Jesus, we will discover answers for our journey.

Step 1: I believe good health will be a witness of my relationship with God.
Step 2: I am not able to live healthy without God.
Step 3: I need other help like First Place for Health.
Step 4: I will choose obedience in what I eat and how I treat my body.

Jesus did not use His position as God to His own advantage. How can overconfidence or pride convince us we don't need His help in our health journey?

_____

_____

_____

Jesus made Himself nothing by humbling Himself as a servant and becoming human. What role does humility play in your food and exercise choices?

_____

_____

_____

Jesus obeyed to death and faced the cross. When you have cravings or a tendency to binge on unhealthy foods, how can you choose to obey like Christ obeyed?

_____

_____

_____

Our God endured the worst, including trauma, temptation, betrayal, grief, torture, hunger, thirst, mocking, nakedness, persecution, execution, rejection, abandonment, isolation, pain, injustice, anguish. He was described in Isaiah 53:3 as "a man of suffering, and familiar with pain." Our suffering should cause us to draw closer to Jesus, though we can't begin to imagine His pain. What does the psalmist say to do in Psalm 50:15?

_____

_____

_____

One of the clearest ways of honoring God is to ask what He wants you to learn during your trial. How you respond to a crisis may be the only way the world around you will see the glory of Jesus.

In her book, *God's Best During Your Worst*, author Robin Luftig quotes Nicolas Wolterstorff, whose faith was stretched to its breaking-point when his 25-year-old son was killed during a mountain-climbing accident. He needed an answer to the question why? Wolterstorff wrote:

"God is not only the God of the sufferers but the God who suffers … . It is said of God that no one can behold his face and live. A friend said perhaps it meant that no one could see his sorrow and live. Or perhaps his sorrow is his splendor. Instead of explaining our suffering, God shares it."

Nothing we do, nor any response to suffering, will ever make God love us more; nor will it make Him love us less. Famed 18th century preacher John Wesley said, "One of the greatest evidences of God's love is that He sends affliction with the grace to bear it."

How does it change your attitude that perhaps your pain and suffering are so the world can see God's glory?

_____

_____

_____

How can your effort to exercise regularly, your sacrifice of unhealthy foods, and your obedience in your health journey help others see God's glory?

_____

_____

_____

Lord, help my life become a beacon that shines out Your glory to the world.

—— DAY 3: THE WILDERNESS

Lord, the struggle is real. You are strength, so please give me a portion of Your strength to face the wilderness. Thank You that You know what is in my future.

My husband and I went to Galveston Bay to help Carole Lewis (director emeritus of First Place for Health) move a few items out of a home she and her husband had there. As we drove toward the house the door opened and Carole came out carrying a huge flat-screen TV.

I said, "Oh, George, you need to get out and help her."
He replied, "She's stronger than I am!"

What made Carole so strong? She works out every week at the gym at her church. And at age 68, she began strength-training. Believe me, she is strong!

We can be strong physically or mentally or emotionally or spiritually. But there is always a reason if we are not strong:

Physically — We gain too much weight or have damaged joints and muscles from accidents or disease

Mentally — We read frivolous writing or do not read at all, or we never try to learn something new

Emotionally — We were abused or betrayed or can't cope, so we allow emotions to rule our life

Spiritually — We don't know and apply the Word or grow into the person God wants us to be

But we can be stronger in all these areas. What are some practical goals you can set to help you grow strong?

Physically

_____
_____
_____

Mentally

_____
_____
_____

Emotionally

_____
_____
_____

Spiritually

_____
_____
_____

Let's review our journey with the nation of Israel.

They had been living in Goshen, Egypt for more than 400 years. God sent Moses to rescue them from Pharaoh's grip, and they left Egypt with his army chasing them; they crossed the Red Sea on the way to a new life of freedom. Let's read an interesting verse about this escape.

"When Pharaoh let the people go, God did not lead them on the road through the Philistine country, though that was shorter" (Exodus 13:17a).

Why do you think God did not lead them on the shortest road? (There's a hint in the verse.)

_____

_____

_____

God led them on the round-about way — through the wilderness — because He knew what would happen on the route through the land of the Philistines. Those fierce warriors were the most barbaric Israel would ever encounter, and God knew the people needed a little toughening up before they faced these bullies. Israel would become mighty if they fought other battles and faced other difficulties first. It would be many years before they challenged the Philistines in battle; if they had encountered them at the beginning of their journey as newly rescued slaves, it would have been too easy to turn back.

Your route may have seemed the most difficult ...
- *Why did my husband die?*
- *Why did he or she leave?*
- *Why did I have to go to work in a secular job to support my family instead of going into ministry right away?*
- *Why did I miss that opportunity?*
- *Why did my child die?*
- *Why did I have cancer or that sickness?*
- *Why was it so difficult financially?*

Your route was the way God led, and it may have been through a terrible desert because He took you away from something much worse. The Israelites needed to learn to trust God, and so did you. God leads us into our personal wilderness to make us stronger.

According to Exodus 14:13-14, what are four benefits we gain from the wilderness journey?
1. Do not _____
2. Stand _____
3. See _____
4. The Lord will _____

How did James describe our wilderness times in James 1:2-4?

_____

_____

_____

What hope did Jesus give in John 16:33 about our wilderness experiences?

_____

_____

_____

The wilderness is the place of encountering God and learning Who He is and what He is willing to do for us.

Lord, thank You for the many times You have led me away from the worst. Help me trust Your wisdom even during difficult situations.

—— DAY 4: THE JOURNEY
Lord, help me remember that the troubles of life happen for me, not to me. Help me overcome defeat and despair by leaning on You and hearing Your voice.

If the Lord takes us through the wilderness to help us become stronger and make us more ready to face life, we must ponder our circumstances seriously — enough to discover what messages He is sending. Instead of feeling sorry for ourselves and grumbling about our difficulties, we can learn to trust God.

What advice would you give your younger self about how to handle a certain situation?

_____

_____

_____

In his monumental paraphrase of the Bible, *The Message*, Eugene Peterson says in Galatians 3:11b: "The person who lives in right relationship with God does it by *embracing what God arranges for him*" (emphasis mine). The word "embrace" includes the concepts of grasping, clutching, grabbing; it also means "enfold" and "entwine." Each of these synonyms gives us a bigger picture of how we should live in difficult times. Grab and hang onto whatever is happening because you know it is part of God's plan for you, and while you are hanging on with dug-in fingernails, you can snuggle up to the horrible event because you understand the beautiful mercy and grace of God.

Let's look at some biblical examples of lessons learned in the wilderness.

****

Jacob

Jacob feared the revenge his brother Esau might exact. Read Genesis 32:22-29. What did Jacob do the night before he was to meet Esau in the wilderness? What lesson do you think Jacob learned?

_____

_____

Moses

In Exodus 3:1-6 Moses saw a bush that was on fire but not consumed. When he investigated, whom did he encounter?

_____

_____

Now read Exodus 3:13-14. What did Moses discover about God in the wilderness?

_____

_____

Elijah

Elijah performed miracles and defeated the prophets of Baal in a spectacular event on Mt. Carmel, but when his life was threatened by Jezebel, he fled to a cave in the desert and wanted to die. God met him in that moment.

Read 1 Kings 19:11-13. What did Elijah learn about God during his time in the wilderness?

_____

_____

****

Jesus

Read Matthew 4:1-11. Whom did Jesus encounter in the wilderness, and how do you think this affected His ministry on Earth?

_____

_____

_____

God taught Jacob to trust during the frightening circumstance of facing his angry brother. God showed Moses that He was the great "I AM" and would supply whatever Moses needed. God revealed Himself as strong and powerful, yet quiet and calm, in the still, small voice Elijah heard in the wilderness, and Elijah knew he need never be afraid of Ahab or Jezebel again. In the wilderness, the devil offered Jesus a quick fix for hunger, the fast-track to fame, and a cut-the-red-tape path to power. But Jesus turned from those temptations to follow the Father into the world to save the world. As soon as Jesus left the wilderness, the Holy Spirit descended on Him at His baptism — Jesus was even better prepared for the world after the wilderness experience. All of us would prefer a shortcut to Christian maturity and a fast-and-easy way of getting healthy, but the Lord knows we will be stronger because of our wilderness experiences.

Which of these biblical encounters reminds you of your battle with healthy eating and weight loss? Why?

_____

_____

_____

Wouldn't it be wonderful if God would simply snap His mighty fingers over us and make us thin and healthy and strong physically, and well balanced and resilient in our emotions? Couldn't He make us super-sharp in our minds, and strong and passionate spiritually?

Instead, He takes us the round-about way through the wilderness of troubles, trials, anxieties, illnesses, failures, suffering. Our wilderness journey helps us understand that each day we need His grace and peace and power.

Read Romans 14:17 and 15:13. What provisions has God given to help us through the wilderness?

_____

_____

_____

Lord, use our wilderness journey to prepare us and make us resilient. Help us set goals to follow You closely but not get caught up in perfectionism. Fill us with empathy for others who are on the journey. Help us never give up because the journey is difficult.

—— DAY 5: MARKERS
Lord, all my life You have been faithful to me. Thank You.

Perhaps you have visited some of the many war memorials in Washington, D.C. The gardens, statues, and tributes to heroes are stunning and moving. We always spend extra time at the Vietnam Veterans Memorial because it is a personal marker of part of our lives. My husband George served in Vietnam as did many of our relatives and friends. On that wall of more than 58,000 names are people whose memories we treasure. We scan one specific panel carefully until we find a name that makes us stop for a while. The name Jessie Wisdom is carved into the granite. We touch it and remember our handsome brother whose bright smile and fun sense of humor filled our lives until the day his helicopter went down. His name on the wall reminds us that he was a great son, brother, husband, father, and soldier. We recall his love of country and family. We shed tears, and we laugh when we remember some of his classic funny lines. The marker of his name helps us celebrate his memory. A memorial is to remember the battles, the heartache, the sadness; but also to treasure the happy moments and joy.

The story of Israel began in brutal slavery. God sent Moses to rescue the people. He opened the Red Sea for their salvation and gave them the promise of a land of milk and honey if they would follow Him. But God didn't lead the Israelites straight there, because the shorter way was more dangerous, and the people had much to learn. After 40 years of wandering in the wilderness, they arrived at the Jordan River and now, because their strength rose up, and they were more willing to obey God, they were ready to cross over. God parted the waters one more time and even though the river was overflowing, they walked across on dry ground. Their new leader, Joshua, told them to set up a memorial.

Read Joshua 4:6-7. Find at least five reasons why building a memorial was a good idea.

Leaving the wilderness calls for a marker that shows the end of wandering and the beginning of abundant life. Memorials remind us of our past and what God has done; they give us hope for the future; they say, "Never forget."

I want to consider the end of our wilderness journey in two ways — spiritual and health. We need markers to identify God's work, and we can build a memorial in our minds.

Spiritual Journey Markers
Marker #1: Remember again the commitment you made to follow Jesus (your Red Sea moment).

_____
_____
_____

Marker #2: Remember when the Holy Spirit has spoken directly to you.

_____
_____
_____

Marker #3: Remember a Bible verse or passage that has challenged or assisted in your walk with God.

_____
_____
_____

Marker #4: Remember one of God's promises you've claimed.

_____
_____
_____

Marker #5: Remember a time when you waited to hear from God.

_____
_____
_____

Marker #6: Remember your calling. What has God asked you to do?

_____
_____
_____

Marker #7: Remember a success in your spiritual life.

_____
_____
_____

Marker #8: Remember a failure in your spiritual life.

_____

_____

_____

As you review these spiritual markers, describe how you will make a new commitment to follow the Lord wholeheartedly:

_____

_____

_____

Healthy Living Journey
Marker #1: Remember when you first heard about and joined First Place for Health.

_____

_____

_____

Marker #2: Remember the sustaining reason for changing your health. How did this impact the four areas of First Place: physical, spiritual, mental, and emotional?

_____

_____

_____

Marker #3: Remember when you first realized you could invite God into your health battles.

_____

_____

_____

Marker #4: Remember how you used to eat and compare it to how you approach food today.

_____

_____

_____

Marker #5: Recall a memory verse you learned in First Place that has continued to impact your health.

_____

_____

_____

Marker #6: Remember your first venture into exercise and describe how moving your body has changed your health.

_____

_____

_____

Marker #7: Remember a success you had in First Place.

_____

_____

_____

Marker #8: Remember a setback in your health journey.

_____

_____

_____

As you review these markers, do you feel your path to wellness has been tough or easy?

It is time to renew our commitment to health. "Renew" means to continue and extend what is working, and make new roads to success. What will you do from this moment on to become stronger?

_____

_____

_____

Lord, sometimes I feel stuck between calling and success — between trusting myself and trusting You. Help me understand that the Christian life and my healthy living journey are filled with battles as well as blessings. You have promised to give us victory. Help me claim that victory today.

—— DAY 6: REFLECTION AND APPLICATION
Lord, thank You for Your almighty power and relentless love for me. I want to know You better and more fully. If knowing You requires me to suffer, I am willing.

God's Miracles

This week we've looked deeply into reasons for suffering, and have discovered some surprising purposes for our wilderness journey and the most difficult parts of our lives. Today is a good day to reflect and meditate on God's strength.

When we see a strong person, we are impressed with their toned and bulging muscles. Let's look at some of God's muscles:

His Grip: John 10:28
His Fingers: Psalm 8:3
His Outstretched Arm: Deuteronomy 26:8
His Right Hand and Holy Arm: Psalm 98:1
His Voice: Job 40:9
His Lifted Arms: John 12:32

God is not like man. He does not have arms and legs and fingers and toes. But the Bible uses these descriptions, called anthropomorphisms, for our benefit so we can get a glimpse of His glory. These terms are not meant to limit or diminish God, but to help us humans get a picture of Him. Write a description of God using your best anthropomorphisms; you can mention His face, hands, arms, breath, hearing, voice, or any other part that helps you fix His image in your mind.

Lord, help me see Your strength so I will lean on You.

—— DAY 7: REFLECTION AND APPLICATION

Lord, as I have reflected on the suffering in my life, my heart is full of love for You in a new way. Thank You for loving me enough to keep me from the hardest paths. Thank You for moments when I have suffered, because I know You have walked with me through the valleys and fires. Remembering has helped me see how much You love me. I am so humbled and grateful.

God is Good

Psalm 119:68 says of God, "You are good, and what you do is good ... ." God never has to choose to be good. In fact, He never thinks about being good — because He is the definition of good. His nature is good. His being is good. Goodness is not an added quality. God blesses us because of His goodness. We have life and joy because of Him. Our food and sustenance are due to His goodness. Our pleasure and purpose are revealed to us because He is good. He rescues, intervenes, protects, guides, delivers — because He is good. And as we have learned this week, even our sorrows, struggles, and suffering are a result of His goodness.

Psalm 31:19a says, "How great is the goodness you have stored up for those who fear you" (NLT). Did you notice the words "stored up?" He has a stockpile of goodness ready to shower on us.

Write a prayer thanking God for His goodness.

_____
_____
_____
_____
_____
_____

Lord, You are good all the time, and all the time You are good. Today, as I walk through my day, show me examples of Your goodness.

WEEK THREE: STRENGTH WILL RISE BECAUSE ... I MAKE A VOW

SCRIPTURE MEMORY VERSE
Then he said to them all: 'Whoever wants to be my disciple must deny themselves and take up their cross daily and follow me. For whoever wants to save their life will lose it, but whoever loses their life for me will save it'. Luke 9:23-24

The Bible is full of contrasts such as " ... when I am weak, then I am strong" and " ... if you want to lead, go last," and the list goes on: " ... those who give will receive," " ... the humble will be exalted," and " ... finding joy in your worst pain." This week's memory verse allows us to peek into God's perspective — what Gracie Malone calls "upside-down truths" in her book, "Life Upside Down." She says these are "two-sided teachings, concepts that cause me to scratch my head and require me to dig deep ... . They seem upside down at first glance, they appear one way but upon further study reveal something exactly opposite. They present the dichotomies of our spiritual life."

As the author of the biblical books of Luke and Acts, "Dr. Luke" pays close attention to details. His writings are logical, chronological, and precise. He was not an eyewitness who walked with Jesus on Earth, but he was a determined investigative reporter who interviewed those who knew Jesus personally and had encounters with the Lord, as well as studying written and oral sources. As a physician and highly educated Gentile, Luke wrote scrupulous details, descriptions, and facts.

When he wrote about the principle of denying self and taking up our cross, Luke seemed to understand how confusing these upside-down principles might be. The Passion Translation uses fresh language for Luke 9:24: "For if you choose self-sacrifice, giving up your lives for my glory, you will discover true life. But if you choose to keep your lives for yourselves, you will lose what you try to keep."

This week we will consider what it means to die to self and commit to life with Jesus. We will see how God uses these upside-down truths in our spiritual growth, and how He nudges us along the journey to good health.

—— DAY 1: AN APPRENTICED DISCIPLE

Lord, what is a disciple and how do I become one? Help me find the path to total devotion to You.

My father-in-law was a master craftsman. When NASA needed some specific parts for the Space Shuttle program, they asked him to make them because he was considered the best machinist in the country. These parts had to be precise — within micro-fractions of an inch. He had recently retired, but they wanted only him to do the work, so they installed an expensive, computerized machine in the garage of his retirement home so he could make the part.

Why was he excellent at his craft? Because he began as an apprentice, and his expertise had grown throughout his life. As a young man he trained next to the best. He watched, asked questions, read books, and practiced skills and proficiencies to become like the masters. He was so excellent at his work, he figured out pages of calculus and trigonometry to check the calculations of the computer before he would trust it to make the Space Shuttle parts.

A disciple of Jesus is an apprentice. We watch the Master, we ask questions, we study His Word, we practice the skills, we follow in His steps. Becoming a disciple is not complicated, but implementing the characteristics of a disciple into your life is not simple either.

Read John 8:31-32. What does Jesus say will make you a true disciple?

_____

_____

_____

What actions do you take each day that help you abide in His Word?

_____

_____

_____

Read 1 John 2:3-6. What does John say is a sign someone is a disciple?

_____

_____

_____

How are you walking with Jesus (apprenticing) in your health journey?

_____

_____

_____

Billy Graham once described a disciple. This is my paraphrase of his famous quote: *A disciple of Jesus is someone who believes in Jesus and follows Him. Sounds simple enough until we realize what else the word disciple means — putting God's Word into action by living the way Christ wants us to live.*

Read Luke 6:40 and 1 Corinthians 11:1. What is our goal as a disciple?

_____

_____

_____

A follower comes after. A disciple learns from the teacher. A true disciple of Jesus asks, "What would Jesus do?" then does it. A disciple listens when Jesus speaks, and obeys what He says.

Read John 13:35. What is one way others will know we are Jesus' disciples?

_____

_____

_____

Have you developed a bond of love for your First Place for Health group? What does that bond mean to you in your health journey?

_____

_____

_____

Read 1 Peter 2:21. Following Jesus' footsteps may not always be easy. How did Christ show us what might be ahead in our discipleship journey?

_____

_____

_____

According to Matthew 4:19 and 2 Timothy 2:2, what did Jesus say He would make of us, and what shall we entrust to others?

_____

_____

_____

Two men were walking toward the village of Emmaus when a third man joined them. The stranger didn't seem to know the latest news, so they told him about how Jesus was crucified in Jerusalem a few days before. I imagine they described the riotous crowds and the horror of the execution. They explained their disappointment and pain when they said, "We had hoped he was the Messiah who had come to rescue Israel" (Luke 24:21a, NLT).

The stranger reminded them of what Moses and the prophets said about how the Messiah would suffer. Then he disappeared.

Read Luke 24:32. What did the two disciples say when they realized the stranger was Jesus, who had risen from the dead that morning? How does it help you determine anything about your discipleship?

_____

_____

_____

Lord, I promise to apprentice with You — to follow Your steps, to love like You love, to reach out to others to help make them disciples too. Help me become the disciple You want me to be.

—— DAY 2: COVENANT
Lord, I want to be Your disciple, but I seem to fail all too often. Help me make an unreserved commitment to You.

Even though the nation of Israel crossed the Jordan River and set up a memorial to remind them what God had done, Joshua knew the people could not go forward into the Promised Land until they had committed themselves completely. God instructed the Israelites to set themselves apart from other nations through the rite of circumcision.

The first mention of circumcision in the Bible is in Genesis 17:9-13, about 13 years after the birth of Ishmael. God reveals Himself as El Shaddai, which means God Almighty. He is the all-sufficient One who rules and reigns supremely. In Genesis 17:2 what does God say He will do?

_____

_____

The rite of circumcision is connected to a covenant. How would you define the word covenant?

_____

_____

_____

Some synonyms for covenant are promise, vow, agreement, contract, or commitment.

There are four major covenants in Scripture.
1. The Noahic Covenant of Genesis 6:18-9:17. God emphasizes the value of human life and promises to never again destroy the Earth with a flood.
2. The Abrahamic Covenant of Genesis 12, 15, and 17. God promises to make Abraham the father of a great nation and to bring redemption to the world through his offspring.
3. The Davidic Covenant of 2 Samuel 7 and 1 Chronicles 17 (also 2 Samuel 23, 2 Chronicles 7:18 and 13:5, Psalm 89:3, and Jeremiah 33:21). God promises to build a house for David — a dynasty — and that his family will reign on the throne of Israel, climaxing with One who will reign forever.
4. The New Covenant in Jeremiah 31:31 and Isaiah 54:10. All God's promises (covenants) are fulfilled in Jesus, the long-awaited Messiah, the ultimate offspring of Abraham — our Redeemer and Savior. This new covenant em phasizes the forgiveness of sin.

Read Hebrews 7:22. Which covenant does the writer say is the best? Why?

_____

_____

_____

Even though for some years circumcision was a preferred medical procedure for baby boys, the religious rite may seem as strange in our Western culture as it did in the time of Joshua. For the Israelites who crossed over into the Promised Land, circumcision was the history of their grandparents and great-grandparents.

Read Joshua 5:5-6, which says the people who left Egypt did not practice circumcision while wandering in the wilderness. What do you see that seems to explain why they failed to follow God's instructions?

_____

_____

_____

Circumcision was given by God to Israel as an outward physical sign that they were a covenant community — ultimately intended to show the repentance, commitment, and vow they had experienced. The parents had wandered in the wilderness because of hard hearts; they had not repented or made vows. Their lack of commitment was a stigma. I can almost hear the mocking from Egyptians who saw them wandering around the wilderness.

Imagine this new generation, hovering on the edge of the Promised Land, ready to follow God wherever He led them. They had crossed the Jordan River with supernatural help from God, and believed they were ready to break the chains of complacency and complaint that had held their parents captive. God asked them to make a personal and physical sacrifice to demonstrate their commitment.

Read Joshua 5:9. What did God say to Joshua?

_____

_____

_____

At that moment in Gilgal (which means "rolled away"), slavery is history. Wandering is over. Shame, complacency, bitterness, and complaining are defeated and taken away. The old generation is gone, and the new generation is poised on the edge of great conquests. They've committed themselves to the Lord as God Almighty.

Choose at least one of the words below and write a sentence that expresses what the younger generation may have been thinking after the ceremony of circumcision.

Yielded   Committed   Dedicated   Faithful   Surrendered

_____

_____

_____

_____

_____

When God first commanded physical circumcision for the Jews, He gave a glimpse into His plans for another, more meaningful kind of circumcision. Read Deuteronomy 30:6. What does God say?

_____

_____

_____

As He looked forward to our modern world, God gave a symbol of what must happen to our hearts. Just as the men of Israel cut away the flesh in circumcision, God will cut away the temptations and desires of the flesh from our hearts, giving us spiritual insight as we become more aware of the eternal. With a circumcised heart, we become more sensitive to others, especially those who need to know Jesus as Savior. Our circumcised hearts detect the move of God and direct us to become stronger so we can serve Him. With our circumcised hearts, we delight in purity, separate ourselves to God, and turn to our one, true God, not idols.

According to Colossians 2:11, who does the work of circumcision of our hearts?

_____

Circumcision was an outward physical sign of a commitment to God. How can healthy body, mind, spirit, and emotions be outward signs to others?

_____

_____

_____

It takes only one generation to eliminate faith. Lord, please help me be strong for my generation and the generations to come.

—— DAY 3: CIRCUMCISION OF THE HEART

Lord, circumcision represents genuine repentance. I ask for Your mighty strength to turn from my old ways and turn toward the new You have planned for me.

If we study the Bible carefully, we discover that circumcision of the heart was the point from the beginning ... not physical circumcision. God mandated that the Jews be circumcised in Genesis 17:10 so they would have a physical reminder of the vow they had made. It reminded them that they were "cut off" from the rest of the world and set apart to serve the One True God.

But the act of circumcision was a symbol that looked forward to our generation, and Deuteronomy 30:6 and Jeremiah 4:4 show us that spiritual circumcision is performed on the heart. After salvation, our heart's desires are for God. We cry out, "Abba, Father" because we long to be close to Him. God has altered our hearts by saving us, and has marked us as His children. Circumcision of the heart is a spiritual cutting-away of everything that does not please God — sin, selfishness, disobedi-

MYPLACE O FOR BIBLE STUDY

ence, and much more. Spiritual circumcision must happen to each one who receives salvation. The Bible says that when we submit our lives fully to God, our hearts are circumcised.

> "A person is not a Jew who is one only outwardly, nor is circumcision merely outward and physical. No, a person is a Jew who is one inwardly; and circumcision is circumcision of the heart, by the Spirit, not by the written code. Such a person's praise is not from other people, but from God" (Romans 2:28-29).

Physical circumcision does not make a person a child of God. Read Matthew 3:9, Genesis 15:6, and Galatians 3:29. What marks us as His children?

_____
_____
_____

When we die to self — refusing to put our desires ahead of God's desires — we leave a mark on our hearts. Circumcision i s a picture of a spiritual truth found in Colossians 3:1-4. Fill in the blanks from these verses:

Set your _____ on things above
For you _____
Your life is now hidden with _____ in God

In Colossians 3:5-8, what does Paul say we must put to death?

_____
_____
_____

Putting off the old, sinful flesh is painful and drastic. The Enemy does not approve of our total commitment to the Lord, so he will cause pain from the "surgery" by reminding us of our sin. It is difficult to heal from circumcision of the heart when he whispers:

~ No one cares
~ You are not number one anymore
~ You gave up too much for Christ
~ You are too old to do this
~ You are too young to do this

What lies has the Enemy whispered to you about your commitment to Jesus?

_____

_____

_____

What lies has the Enemy whispered to you about your battle for wellness and fitness?

_____

_____

_____

In Colossians 3:12-16, how does Paul say we must clothe our new self?

_____

_____

_____

The list is a full "wardrobe" of emotions, mindsets, virtues, and heart changes. Choose one of the articles of clothing Paul mentions and how you can add it to your life.

_____

_____

_____

People in your world need your light, and they need to see your scars and how you have healed with the help of Jesus. Our identity in Christ is not based on our failures, because Christ calls us to be His disciples, His ambassadors, and conquerors. But we must put on the new clothes and be willing to show the scars of our journey.

There is no better way to shine your light to the world than to show that you are transformed. Can people see forgiveness, generosity, love, joy, and peace in the new you? Have you lost weight or built muscles or developed a healthier lifestyle? These outward appearances prove that your heart has been circumcised.

Name some trait — a new kindness, a new way of speaking, a new way of dealing with conflict — you have developed since following the Lord fully.

_____

_____

_____

Name some new appearance (weight loss, strong muscles, more exercise) that shows you are following the Lord in your health and wellness.

_____

_____

_____

Lord, a lamp has the ability to shine but doesn't until it is plugged into the power source. Help me wake up every morning and make Hell regret that I plugged into You as my spiritual power source.

—— DAY 4: A NEW IDENTITY
Lord, I praise You because You have given me new life and new purpose. Help me follow You.

The late President Ronald Reagan once said, "Freedom is never more than one generation away from extinction. We didn't pass it to our children in the blood-stream. It must be fought for, protected, and handed on ... ."

We've seen how one generation pulled away from God and roamed the wilderness for 40 years, leaving the next generation to figure it out for themselves. Now we will look at what we can do to pass along the Truth of God's Word, and the healthy habits we have learned in First Place, to those around us and those who will come after.

Wilderness Christians wander aimlessly with a survivor mentality; they claim to be God's child, but have never fully committed to Him and hang on to their carnal mindset. I lived the life of a wandering Christian in my early adulthood. I craved success in the corporate world and all the trappings of that success in my private life. I served in the church with gusto, joining lots of committees, and working hard on church programs. I read my Bible and every popular book on Christianity. But I was what Phillip Keller, in his book, "Walking With God," calls "halfway people," living with one foot in and one foot out.

I faced a moment of transformation when I met a group of fully committed Christian women who lived intentionally and moved in victory. This Bible study group was filled with women from other denominations, of all ages and backgrounds, who had two goals: 1) to know the Word of God fully and 2) to bring their neighbors to Jesus. I discovered that living in victory meant making personal sacrifices and understanding who God wants me to become.

For the Israelites that moment of transformation came when they submitted to circumcision. We must all make a decision of enormous spiritual impact if we are going to follow Christ.

Read Matthew 22:37. What is one of our first commitments in following the Lord? Why do you think this is necessary?

_____

_____

_____

Read Hebrews 11:6. What pleases God? Write a personal definition of "faith."

_____

_____

_____

Read Psalm 143:10. Write in your words a prayer that expresses the thoughts of this Psalm.

_____

_____

_____

David wrote in Psalm 37:5 that if we commit our way to the Lord and trust in Him, He will "do this." I want to follow Him fully and trust His ways — no matter how slow or illogical they may seem.

Describe a time when God made a way when there seemed to be no way.

_____

_____

_____

Many of our personal First Place for Health stories run parallel to the plight of the wandering Christian, but in a physical manifestation — we allowed unhealthy eating and sedentary habits to creep into the way we lived. That's why we came to FP4H. Maybe busyness or heartache or illness played a part in weight-gain and a weak body, but if we are honest, most of us became unhealthy because we made poor choices or were complacent, and some of us have been downright rebellious about making good health decisions. Those of us who have been in First Place for years may attend meetings and work through Bible studies, yet we are complacent about following the program. We are wandering in the wilderness — thinking we are following God, but not on the path toward wholeness and wellness.

The Israelites' commitment at the moment of circumcision shows vulnerability — a willingness to make a personal, physical sacrifice for the sake of being identified as God's. Let's take a moment of private openness and personal honesty about our health journey with these intimate questions:

Am I following the First Place for Health program fully and completely? Or ... have I allowed myself to wander in the wilderness of complacency?

_____
_____
_____

Have I read the history and purpose behind FP4H, and do I pray for and support the ministry? Or ... have I never asked how it was built or been concerned about its future?

_____
_____
_____

Have I truthfully and diligently tracked my food intake? Or ... have I been lazy about recording every food I've eaten, and even changed the tracker to look good to my leader?

_____
_____
_____

Have I studied *My Place for Nutrition* and adjusted the type and quality of food I eat because I've seen the value of a well-balanced food plan? Or ... do I eat whatever food and whatever amount I want without thinking of the calories or the Live It food plan?

_____
_____

Have I read *My Place for Fitness* and implemented moving into my daily life? Or ... have I made excuses for why I can't exercise?

_____

_____

_____

Have I worked through the *My Place for Discovery* books, which help me understand my emotional and mental triggers for unhealthy eating? Or ... have I thought they were too difficult? Am I afraid to do this kind of self-discovery?

_____

_____

_____

Have I followed the recipes and suggestions for healthy food substitutes to my high-fat/high-sugar diet? Or ... do I continue to buy the same processed foods? Describe why you make these choices.

_____

_____

_____

What does Romans 12:1-2 tell us to do with our physical bodies? What do you think the term "living sacrifice" means?

_____

_____

_____

The recipients of Paul's letter might have been surprised at the words "living sacrifice." They were accustomed to bringing an animal to the altar, which would die to temporarily pay for their sins. Because of Christ's death on the cross, there was no longer a need for an animal sacrifice.

Now, we become the sacrifice as we live in gratitude for Christ's once-for-all payment for our sins. As we live each day, we offer every part of ourselves to Him — our hands and feet; our eyes, ears, and mouth; our mind and actions. A living sacrifice is always ready to speak for Christ and give grace and encouragement to others. Our readiness identifies us as people who belong to Christ.

When Joshua commanded that the Israelites be circumcised, he knew they would be more completely identified as God's nation, free from Egypt's slavery and done with wilderness wandering. In the last 40 years they had not seen themselves as covenant people or known God as their covenant God, but now they are renewed and ready for Him to lead. This moment of commitment changed their identity and future.

What about you? Are you ready to stop wandering in the wilderness of up-and-down weight-loss or stop-and-start exercise or in-and-out Bible study? Write a commitment to the Lord to start the First Place for Health program anew, with a refreshed and revitalized commitment to following God into health.

_____

_____

_____

Lord, I want to pass on a legacy of quality living, eating, exercising, and spiritual habits. I do not want to wander in the wilderness or live a complacent, unfulfilled life. Please shine the light on my path and help me identify with You in my spiritual walk and in my First Place journey.

—— DAY 5: BUT WHAT ABOUT THE HITTITES?

Lord, help me search my heart, and give me the courage to enter those rooms there that I have concealed and ignored. I want to sever all ties to the hidden and unheeded.

My husband came out of the testing facility with a big smile on his face. "I nailed it," he said. His doctor had ordered a treadmill test to see why George seemed out of breath when he exerted himself like mowing the lawn. But he was proud of the way he had pushed himself on the treadmill and exceeded his goals for speed and duration. Later that evening, his doctor called to say the test revealed a big problem in the artery that leads into the heart. He referred us to a cardiac specialist, who performed an angioplasty. Hidden and unknown, a collection of plaque in his heart held the power of life or death, but after the doctor removed it, George's breathing, energy, and strength increased in a fresh, new way.

Spiritually we may have a room hidden in our heart where we don't want to go. We have the door closed and sealed. Behind that door is our "no-man's land."

Moses, the great leader and man of God, had died and his aide, Joshua, would take the leading role in the nation of Israel. God spoke to Joshua, giving him instructions about next steps. What did He say in Joshua 1:1-4?

_____

_____

God set the boundaries of the land that would forever be the homeland of the Jews — from the southern border of the Negev desert area, to the Lebanon mountains in the north; and from the Euphrates River in the east, to the Mediterranean Sea in the west. And He promised in verse 5, "I will never leave you nor forsake you."

Read Ephesians 1:4-8 and write the promise of God.

_____

_____

_____

In Joshua 1:3-4, after God gives the expanses of the Promised Land, He adds, " ... including all the land of the Hittites" (NLT).

At that time, the two largest countries in the area were Egypt and Syria, each claiming large expanses of land — Egypt to the south and Syria to the north of Canaan. These two mighty nations were in a constant state of war. Scholars believe there was a kind of "no-man's land" between the two — a "neutral zone" to reduce constant border skirmishes — and that the Hittites had moved into this area. We need to understand why God added the caveat " ... including all the land of the Hittites."

Imagine Joshua poised over a table with a large map of the area, planning his conquest of Canaan. He would immediately pinpoint the large cities as targets, and circle places that had resources such as water, mines, and food. He would identify the high ground, knowing he needed to take those strategic points.

He might skip over the Hittites as he developed his strategy — they seemed unimportant and certainly not strategic; it was a place for misfits and stragglers — and secrets — and didn't look too big or imposing. Perhaps it was an area they could deal with later.

But God said He wanted it taken too.

I wonder what territory God has given you and me that we let sit idle because it's always been that way or *it's just part of life* or *there's nothing I can do about it anyway*. Our no-man's land might be a habit we can't seem to conquer or a person with whom we can't seem to reconcile. No-man's land might be a food addiction or procrastination. Or frantic busyness or a need to control. Our land of the Hittites could show up as an inner deadness or spiritual sleepwalking. We ignore it because if we concentrate on the parts of the Christian life we can conquer — Bible reading, prayer, serving at church — we feel good about ourselves and the image we are projecting. As Mark Buchanan wrote in his book, "Your God is Too Safe:"

> " ... we learn much about God and at the same time grow distant from God; we will study the intricacies of doctrine but lose passion; we will become eloquent at God talk, but cease talking to God."

As we face our Promised Land of peace, rest, and healing, we must never forget to conquer our personal land of the Hittites — the parts of our lives we have stuffed away into a safe borderland.

Match the following verses by drawing a line to the feelings and emotions we tend to hide away in our secret no-man's land.

Philippians 4:6	Anger
Isaiah 41:10	Bitterness
Matthew 6:14-15	Anxiety
Hebrews 12:15	Fear
Psalm 55:22	Unforgiveness
Ecclesiastes 7:9	Burdens

Choose one of those emotions/feelings and write about how it plays a role in your life, and if you think you have hidden it away in no-man's land.

_____

_____

_____

I've discovered some other secrets hidden away in my no-man's land. In my personal First Place for Health journey, I had a breakthrough victory over sweets as I worked through *My Place for Discovery*; but I replaced my enormous cravings for sweet and creamy with a new snack. Now in my pantry you will find a bag of tortilla chips. I munch a bowl of these when I feel stressed or bored. I love these salty, crunchy delights even more if I melt cheddar cheese on top for a quick nacho treat. I've allowed the chips to reside in the no-man's land where I ask myself, *Does it really hurt if I eat this snack? How bad can it be? If no one sees me eat these, do the calories count?*

We can shove any part of our health journey into no-man's land, because we don't think anyone will notice, because we can deal with it later, because it seems unimportant.

What activity, habit, or secret have you put in your no-man's land?

_____

_____

_____

God is calling us to include the "land of the Hittites" in our conquests — to claim the entirety of His promises. What is your no-man's land? Have you ignored God's command to master it?

Lord, I claim the promises of Your Word, and I want to conquer all the territory You have given me. Give me strength and courage, I pray.

—— DAY 6: REFLECTION AND APPLICATION

Lord, too often I think only of myself and what is on my "to-do" list. Help me slow down my activities and change my selfish desires to longings to spend more time with You.

Do I need more time?

A recent study calculated how much time we spend each year: 122 days either asleep or at home and 87 days at work or school; the balance is divided between entertainment and hobbies (59 days), eating (39 days), hanging out with friends (31 days), and in the car (21 days). All that activity leaves six days for church or time with God, which is less than two hours each week.

I've always felt time was my enemy. There's never enough of it. It flies. It runs out. We can kill time but not stop it. And as Harvey Mackay said, "Time is free, but it's priceless. You can't own it, but you can use it. You can't keep it, but you can spend it. Once you've lost it you can never get it back."

According to John Mark Comer in his book, "The Ruthless Elimination of Hurry," the solution isn't more time. Comer writes, "I catch myself saying, 'I wish there were ten more hours in a day.' Even as I mouth it, I realize my logic is flawed ... what would I do with those ten hours? The same thing most people would do — fill them."

Today, keep a log of how much time you spend on each activity. Study the entries. How have you spent your time on worthy effort and how have you wasted it?

Lord, help to take a hard look at where I spend my valuable and limited time. Guide me to discern which activities are worthy effort and which are wasted.

—— DAY 7: REFLECTION AND APPLICATION

Lord, we know purpose and grace are Your gifts to us. Forgive us for living too long without discovering Your plans. Help us make a vow to desire the holy life You have called us to.

Making Time For My Soul

A British traveler landed in Africa, intent on a rapid journey into the jungle. He hired some local porters to carry his supplies. After an exhausting day of travel and a fitful night's sleep, he was eager to resume the trip the next morning. But the porters refused to move. He could not bribe, cajole, or plead enough to get them started. The foreman finally told him, "They are waiting for their souls to catch up with their bodies."

Our memory verse this week calls us to "take up (our) cross daily and follow" Jesus, but we can't until we have made time for our souls and minds to catch up to our busy lifestyles.

Read and meditate on Psalm 61 at least three times today. Write your paraphrase for all or part of it.

WEEK FOUR: STRENGTH WILL RISE BECAUSE ... I WAIT

SCRIPTURE MEMORY VERSE
And God is able to bless you abundantly, so that in all things at all times, having all that you need, you will abound in every good work. 2 Corinthians 9:8

I'm not good at waiting. Not at a red light and not in a long line at the grocery store. My husband is the champion of slow. Yours too? We should talk. Waiting is a problem for me. I flit from line to line trying to find the fastest one. I cut through back streets when traffic is stalled. I know it probably doesn't save time, but I feel as if I must do something to speed up.

I know the best way to lose weight is 1-2 pounds a week, but slow-and-steady takes weeks and months to get to my goal weight. So I try fad diets, leaving out whole food groups, to accomplish faster weight loss. And you know the rest of the story — the weight comes back as fast as it comes off.

I also don't want to wait on God to transform me. I'd like to be everything He wants me to be, but could we just hurry it up, please? In her book, "Passion and Purity," Elisabeth Elliot says, "Waiting on God requires the willingness to bear uncertainty, to carry within oneself the unanswered question, lifting the heart to God about it whenever it intrudes upon one's thoughts." Let's think about her words phrase by phrase.

The willingness to bear uncertainty. For sure, uncertainty is the most difficult part — not knowing how the situation is going to turn out. I may think (some would say worry) about the conclusion, but I'm often not willing to be in the dark about outcomes and resolutions.

To carry within oneself the unanswered question. I'm more like the five-year-old who stamps her foot because she wants answers now, than I am like a follower of Jesus who is willing to carry unanswered questions.

Lifting the heart to God about it whenever it intrudes upon one's thoughts. I know prayer and trust in God lead me to peace, but I act out, impatient and manipulative, so I won't have to wait.

This familiar verse in Isaiah promises the waiting is worth it — if we are waiting on God.

> "Even youths grow tired and weary, and young men stumble and fall; but those who hope in the LORD will renew their strength. They will soar on wings like eagles; they will run and not grow weary, they will walk and not be faint" (Isaiah 40:30-31).

—— DAY 1: RESTING WHILE YOU WAIT

Lord, I don't know how to rest, especially when I'm waiting. Even when I think I've slept well or relaxed enough, I need You to show me the still waters where my soul can rest.

My grandmother had a featherbed. You sank when you got into it, as the fluffy mattress came up all around you. It was wonderful, but there was one problem — the bed was built on a frame with slats instead of box springs.

Slats are planks of wood stretched across a frame. Open-wire springs are placed on the slats and the mattress is put on top, like an earlier version of box springs and mattresses ... only dustier. In grandmother's featherbed, one of the slats was barely long enough to fit across. If the bed moved slightly the wrong way, the slat slipped off and fell to the floor. If you were in the bed, you crashed too. To be safe in that bed, you had to lie still; no thrashing about or cuddling down — as if you couldn't put your full weight on it. As wonderful as that featherbed felt, no one could really rest in it.

I'm sure you don't have that trouble with your beds at home. Your bed's foundation supports the mattress and holds you firmly. When you lie down, you can exhale and fully relax. You totally depend and rest your body on a solid bed with a box spring.

Israel had wandered on the brink of the Promised Land for 40 years before Joshua became their leader. Hebrews equates the Promised Land with rest.

Read Hebrews 3:16-19. Why didn't the first generation of Israelites enter into the Promised Land?

_____

_____

Rest is more than sleep or a great vacation. True rest is falling into the arms of God with full assurance that He is in control.

Their grandparents were captive slaves. Their parents were aimless wanderers. Now the Israelites had the opportunity to accept God's promise of rest.

According to Hebrews 4:1, what is the status of God's promised rest today?

_____

_____

_____

You and I can enter into God's rest. It is the spiritual rest we find in Christ when we surrender to Him. The road to finding God's rest is paved with faith.

Come to Jesus. Read Matthew 11:28. What do we receive when we come to Him?

_____

_____

Salvation rest is your Red Sea moment.

Yield to Jesus. Read Matthew 11:29-30. When we yield to Him, we discover His yoke is easy. What do we find?

_____

_____

Taking Jesus' easy yoke is your Jordan River moment.

Another word for rest is peace. Read Romans 5:1. What peace does it say we have?

_____

_____

Jesus removes all obstacles so even though we were once at war with God, we can now have peace with Him.

Find the Peace of God
Read Philippians 4:6-8 from the New Living Translation: "Don't worry about anything ..." (vs. 6a).

Fill in the blank.

1) Don't _____ about anything.

Anxiety and worry are harmful to your health because they trigger stress hormones that can make your heart beat faster and harder — inflaming blood vessels, raising cholesterol, and causing other problems. Headaches, depression, breathing difficulty, and fatigue are only a few symptoms caused by stress and anxiety.
What worries you?

_____

_____

_____

vs. 6b: " ... instead, pray about everything. Tell God what you need, and thank him for all he has done.

vs. 7: "Then you will experience God's peace, which exceeds anything we can understand. His peace will guard your hearts and minds as you live in Christ Jesus.

vs. 8: "And now, dear brothers and sisters, one final thing. Fix your thoughts on what is true, and honorable, and right, and pure, and lovely, and admirable. Think about things that are excellent and worthy of praise."

Fill in the rest of the blanks from this passage.

2) Pray about _____

3) Tell God _____

4) Thank Him for _____

5) Fix your _____

6) Think about _____ and _____

Looking through these instructions from Paul, which do you need to follow and why?

_____

_____

_____

Based on verse 7, describe in your own words the peace of God.

_____

_____

_____

The only path to God's rest is faith. The key is to quit trying in our strength and allow God to do everything. He made us. He knows how to manage us. We can rest in Him and trust ourselves to Him. That means we can get rid of every burden, whether it is related to health, reputation, work, house, children, ministry, business, etc.

Lord, I am grateful for peace with You because I have trusted Jesus as my Savior, and I long for the peace of God, which I receive by trusting You.

—— DAY 2: WORKING WHILE YOU WAIT
Lord, please give me courage and inspiration to plan and produce while I wait for the day You tell me to move forward.

Waiting is not about sitting still. If we are following Jesus, we know there are blessed experiences in our future, but sitting on our haunches doing nothing — feeling stagnant, waiting for the blessings to fall on us like some glittery mist — is not the path to success. We may need to be preparing for the days to come — while we wait.

Joshua had two jobs while the nation of Israel waited on the banks of the Jordan. The first was to get a commitment from the three tribes that claimed land on the east side of the river.

Read Joshua 1:12-15. What are the names of these tribes and what were the conditions Moses imposed when he granted the land?

_____

_____

_____

Why do you think Joshua felt it necessary to obtain their commitment again?

_____

_____

_____

Joshua's second task was to send spies to Jericho. Read Joshua 2:1. How many did he send?

_____

How does this compare to the number of spies Moses sent out 40 years earlier (Numbers 13)? Why do you think Joshua sent only two this time?

_____

_____

_____

When we spend our waiting-time busy for the Lord, we exhibit faith. If we analyze faith, we discover it typically is about not knowing. We don't know the outcome, nor do we know what to expect, but we depend on God in faith anyway. And while we are trusting, we do everything we can to be prepared and get in touch with the mind and heart of God.

Like a family that loved to work jigsaw puzzles — when they finished one, the mom would gather up the pieces in a plastic bag and throw away the box-lid. If they ever tried to work the puzzle again, they had no picture to go by. Faith is that way — like putting the puzzle together with no picture.

As we wait, we must decide to exercise our faith and do all we can. How will you obey God, and what are you willing to do to obey Him while you wait on Him?

- Will you give up unhealthy food choices so you will be a positive witness to others?
- Will you take time to exercise so your body will be strong?
- Will you work through First Place Bible studies to learn more about God?
- Will you do off-stage, behind-the-scenes work at church?
- Will you reach out to the "unpopular" people around you?
- Will you help a newbie get started in First Place for Health?
- Will you give away your stuff or show kindness just for the sake of serving Christ?
- Will you keep praying for that miracle that seems impossible?

Pick one of these questions and write a plan for what you will do as you wait.

_____

_____

_____

_____

_____

Lord, I don't like to wait, but I see how You can use my waiting times to prepare me for the purpose and future You have for me. Change my attitude about waiting and build a new desire in me for working while I wait.

—— DAY 3: HEALING WHILE YOU WAIT
Lord, You are my wellness and my healing. Speak to my aching heart. Sooth my weary soul. Guide me to healing.

Researchers say there are five types of healing
1) Physical — of the body
2) Emotional — of the heart
3) Mental — of the mind
4) Spiritual — of the soul (the inner person)
5) Holistic — of body, heart, mind, and soul

This sounds like what we have learned in First Place for Health. In fact, its mission statement describes the whole person approach: "To provide a biblical wellness program that enables individuals to achieve balance in spirit, soul, mind and body based on giving Christ first place."

The FP4H website explains that the key word in the statement is "balance" because we tend to compartmentalize, only addressing one area at a time. But healthy living requires us to harmonize the four. What does Jesus say in Mark 12:30 about the four-sided person?

_____

_____

_____

I struggled for more than a year with chronic back pain, until one of my hips was replaced with a titanium prosthesis; my focus during that time was physical misery. For months after the death of my mother I wrestled with grief, so my focus was emotional. When I lost my job, my battles were mental as I wondered what I would do with the rest of my life. Conflict at church sent me down a path of spiritual agony as I fought my way back to trusting God instead of people.
Which of the four is your main struggle today? Why?

_____

_____

_____

The quest for healing requires us to compare conventional, worldly wisdom with God's solutions. Look up these verses to see His answer to worldly wisdom on healing.

What the World Says:	What God Says:
Self-love/Self-promotion	Psalm 139:14 _____
Identity in what I do	Ephesians 1:3-6 _____
Dependent on circumstances	Proverbs 3:5 _____
Self-examination	Isaiah 54:17 _____
Solitude	1 Chronicles 16:11 _____
Mindfulness	2 Corinthians 10:5 _____
Nature soothes the soul	1 Samuel 12:24 _____

Healing while we wait means we follow God's way and plan for restoration, not the counterfeit ways offered by the world. Let's list some practical steps to healing.

1) **The Word of God.** Read, memorize, and meditate. Find a way to get the truth of the Bible into your heart, mind, soul, and body. Perhaps you need a reading plan for the entire Bible; or focus on one book at a time, delving deeply into its message. Maybe you need to study topically, choosing one subject to search from cover to cover.

2) **Prayer.** Learn more about prayer by reading books and studying verses about it. Find a way to pray that fits your lifestyle. Perhaps you need to set an alarm at a certain time of day for prayer. Perhaps you need to purchase a notebook or journal and designate it for prayer, writing out the words you want to say to the Lord. Maybe you need a prayer partner to meet with on a regular basis. Or consider prayer-walking, praying for your neighborhood as you pass the houses.

3) **Friends.** Develop friendships with people who are authentic and vulnerable so you can share your deepest thoughts and feelings. Ask God to reveal that person to you, and be intentional about interacting to help you heal.

Consider other practical steps you can take toward healing while you wait.

4) _____

_____

_____

5) _____

_____

_____

Healing while we wait depends on our relationship with God during the waiting period. Here are two relationship building-blocks.

1) Confess my sin and ask for cleansing.

   Psalm 66:18 says, "If I had cherished sin in my heart, the Lord would not have listened."

   Confess means to recognize and admit — acknowledge and declare. One synonym is blurt out. Confession is a quick response — as soon as I say it or do it or think it, I tell God I'm sorry.

2) Allow Him to mold me and make me.

   Isaiah 64:8 says, "Yet You, LORD, are our Father. We are the clay, You are the potter; we are all the work of Your hand."

   Molding takes time. God uses our circumstances, good and bad, to sculpt us into the person He wants us to be.

What goals will you set for yourself this week to allow God to use these building-blocks of confession and molding?

Lord, You are the great physician. Please spread Your healing power over me as I wait for You.

—— DAY 4: GETTING TO KNOW JESUS WHILE YOU WAIT

Lord, I want to know You. Please reveal Yourself to me. I know about You because I've read about Your life on Earth, and I know You are the Son of God. But I want to know You as a dear and close friend.

Israel captured the land east of the Jordan, crossed the river, and built the memorial to God's faithfulness — but God called them to total commitment through circumcision. Part of the reason was to "roll away the reproach" of previous years of disobedience and unbelief (Joshua 5:6-9).

Now the people were ready to move into the conquest of the Promised Land and Joshua was ready to lead them, but he needed one more touch from God and one more affirmation that the Lord would be with them.

Read Joshua 5:13-15, which records one of the times Jesus made a personal appearance in the Old Testament. He didn't suddenly show up on Earth when Mary gave birth to Him — He has always been in existence. Where do the following verses say He was active on Earth?

Colossians 1:15-16

Genesis 18:1-8

Genesis 32:24-32

Daniel 3:25

Revelation 1:8

Jesus' appearance is called a Christophany — a preincarnate, physical manifestation. God had promised to be with Joshua in 1:5b: "For I will be with you as I was with Moses. I will not fail you or abandon you" (NLT). Now the promise comes true as Jesus shows up to encourage and inspire Joshua.

At first Joshua didn't recognize him (5:13). His first instinct was to find out if the man was for Israel or its enemies. How did the man answer in verse 14?

When Joshua heard him speak he recognized the voice of the Lord, and fell face down in reverence and removed his shoes in awe. Whatever we accomplish for the Lord or whatever ministry we undertake, our power and public successes or victories are always won in private when we submit to the Lord in devotion, respect, adoration, and wonder of Him who created and sustains us.

In his book, "Be Strong (Joshua)," Warren Wiersbe says, "It is doubtful that anybody in the camp of Israel knew about their leader's meeting with the Lord, but that meeting made the difference between success and failure on the battlefield."

How does becoming intimate with Jesus help you in your relationship with others?

_____

_____

_____

How does becoming intimate with Jesus enhance your First Place for Health journey?

_____

_____

_____

If your calendar is filled with appointments, it can be difficult to fit in time with God. If your spare time is filled with work-related reading and activities, you will starve your deepest soul connection with Jesus. If your mind is filled with worry, your body will react with aches and pains and disease. If you try to please everyone, you will develop a slave mentality.

Jesus changed the world in three years. Yet He never hurried even though there were crowds around and people pressing against Him. He was busy — preaching, healing, casting out demons — but He often disappeared to a quiet place. Mark 1:35 says He went out by Himself early in the morning; in Mark 6:31-32, He withdrew from the crowds to rest; in Matthew 14:23, He spent time alone with the Father for spiritual renewal.

We need daily time with Jesus, and we need periodic times of rest and renewal. Developing a daily quiet time is vital to your health and wellness. Consider your calendar and the routines of those in your household to figure out what time of day is best for you. For some, setting an alarm to wake up before anyone else in the house is perfect for meeting with Jesus. For others, the best time is evening when the household has settled in for the night. For moms of little ones, the best quiet time may be when children are napping in the afternoon. The time of day is not important; having an intentional appointment with Jesus is what matters.

What seems to work best for your lifestyle and schedule?

_____

_____

Setting aside an extended time to spend with the Lord requires a different commitment and discipline than a daily quiet time. I like to take a full day or more each quarter to spend seeking God; my friend Cindy Martin calls it "sitting with my Savior." And that is what I try to do. One quarter, I attend a First Place for Health "Wellness Week" that includes time with friends and worship, but allows for hours and hours alone with the Word and the Lord. One quarter, I go to the beach for a day and a night; there is something about the constant sound and movement of the waves that replenishes my spiritual rhythms. One quarter, we join with another couple at a mountain cabin to have fun playing games and taking hikes, and make time for deep prayer together. One quarter, I designate a day at home for thanksgiving and praise; we don't turn on any electronic devices, and spend every awake moment finding ways to adore our Creator.

Write ideas about how you could sit with your Savior for an extended time each quarter.

Jan/Feb/Mar   _____

Apr/May/June _____

July/Aug/Sept _____

Oct/Nov/Dec   _____

Read Isaiah 40:30-31. How does this passage say that waiting is not draining or tiring, but renewing?

_____

_____

_____

Lord, You are the forever, eternal God, and we thank You for working in us while we wait. Thank You for showing up when we need You most.

—— DAY 5: CELEBRATING WHILE YOU WAIT

Lord, there is nothing like a party to infuse joy into our souls. Help us remember like Israel remembered and celebrate like they celebrated.

When I was working in the corporate world I had a client in Sweden. He and his wife became personal friends of my family. He was curious about the American way of life and our celebrations and traditions. One fall he asked about the upcoming Thanksgiving holidays, and I told him about the pilgrims and the harvest. But he was more interested in our modern celebration habits, which I had to admit were mostly watching hours of football and eating enormous amounts of food. I wanted to show him how nostalgic we are about the provision of God and the bounty of the harvest, but he ended up hearing more about college rivalries, and turkey and dressing vs. turkey and stuffing.

"On the evening of the fourteenth day of the month, while camped at Gilgal on the plains of Jericho, the Israelites celebrated the Passover" (Joshua 5:10).

Before Moses died, he told the nation to never forget that they were once slaves in Egypt, and how God had delivered them from bondage. Passover is the celebration that looks back at Egypt and remembers God's rescue. He wanted the Israelites to remember they were a redeemed people, but it seems the generation that crossed the Red Sea neglected this great celebration. Only once during the wilderness journey does the Bible say they commemorated Passover (Numbers 9:1-14). Their sin of rebellion prevented them from following God in this great festival tradition. Now Joshua led them to remember and observe it.

Today, Jews mark Passover with a big celebration, loads of preparation, and a time for overeating. It symbolizes rebirth, spring, and the journey from slavery to freedom. According to the Torah, Passover is held for seven days beginning on the 15th of Nissan, typically April on our modern calendar. The day is filled with stories of the nation escaping slavery, while rabbis and fathers tell each family's exodus story.

When the nation was held in slavery in Egypt, what did God say to Pharaoh (Exodus 8:1-2)?

_____

_____

_____

Pharaoh refused, so God sent 10 plagues. According to Exodus 11:4-7, what was the last plague?

_____

_____

_____

How did a family keep the death angel from their household (Exodus 12:3, 7, 12-13)?

_____

_____

_____

The theme of Passover — and of the Lord's Supper — is always salvation. Christians don't celebrate Passover in the Jewish way, but Jesus told us to celebrate the Lord's Supper (Communion) because He fulfilled all the types and prophecies of the Hebrew Scriptures. He is the Lamb. He is redemption. He is the Savior. We look back at our redemption and celebrate the great gift of salvation.

How do you and your family (including your church family) celebrate Communion? What does it mean to you personally?

_____

_____

_____

Lord, You are my Passover Lamb. You have rescued me from the bondage of sin. I celebrate You. I remember Your sacrifice. I honor You as my Savior.

—— DAY 6: REFLECTION AND APPLICATION

Lord, waiting is more difficult than I thought. I am beginning to understand that it isn't just sitting still, but resting in Your strength and wisdom.

Waiting Well

Today let's ponder a bit more about waiting. It's not like sitting on a park bench, twiddling our thumbs, doing nothing. Instead, waiting should be purposeful and resolute. What have you learned about waiting that you never thought of before?

_____

_____

_____

In this list, circle barriers that keep you from waiting well:

What's undone	The to-do list
Guilt	I'm compelled to work
The should's	I'm busy

Lord, my heart longs for You. My mind knows You know what is best. My soul hungers for Your wisdom. My body is ready to obey. Please remove any barriers I have set up. Help me wait with eager anticipation of Your power and purpose in my life.

—— DAY 7: REFLECTION AND APPLICATION

Lord, I need strength to wait well. Fill me with Your power for the waiting time.

My Waiting To-Do List
1) Choose praise and worship instead of complaint
2) Retell to friends and family stories of God's intervention
3) Remember God bestows honor upon those who seek no glory for themselves
4) Thank Jesus for being the Passover Lamb
5) Put sin away, just as the bread has no leaven to puff it up

What will you add?

6) _____

7) _____

Lord, I will be stronger even though I am waiting. Help me believe and trust You in each waiting moment.

WEEK FIVE: STRENGTH WILL RISE BECAUSE ... I OBEY

SCRIPTURE MEMORY VERSE
Therefore everyone who hears these words of mine and puts them into practice is like a wise man who built his house on the rock. Matthew 7:24

In a short period of time, we have followed Israel as they broke camp on one side of the Jordan River and walked behind the Ark of the Covenant on dry ground. The people built a memorial after making the decision to follow God into the Promised Land. They faced and defeated the enemy of fear, made a vow to God to be His people, and agreed to be circumcised as a sign of devotion. We've followed their path of healing, resting, waiting, and celebrating.

It feels as if they are ready to conquer the land, but God has at least one more lesson to teach the people — and us.

No one had ever heard of manna until the Israelites found a white, wafer-like, honey-flavored substance on the ground one morning after they crossed the Red Sea. According to Exodus 16, the people complained about conditions in the wilderness and longed for the food they'd had in Egypt — forgetting the cruel slavery of that place. So the Lord sent food from Heaven. They called it manna, which means, "what is it?"

Read Numbers 11:8. What did the Israelites do with this bread from Heaven?

_____

_____

_____

According to Deuteronomy 8:3 and Psalm 105:40, why did God send the manna each day?

_____

_____

_____

—— DAY 1: PROVISION AND OBEDIENCE
Lord, help me grow into maturity as I trust You to provide and learn to obey You.

Read Joshua 5:11. What happened on the day after the Passover celebration?

_____

_____

According to Joshua 5:12, what was unusual about eating the produce of the land?

_____

_____

God met the physical need of His people by sending a daily portion of heavenly bread. Never once did they wake up to find it hadn't "rained" manna; never once did God fail to provide. He taught them to trust His hand of provision by giving just enough for each day.

What kind of lesson can we learn from God's daily provision?

_____

_____

_____

Describe a time when you desperately needed His provision.

_____

_____

_____

As Israel entered Canaan, the barley harvest was in full swing and grain was plentiful. The people may have purchased it, or perhaps the inhabitants had fled to Jericho for safety and left the grain behind. This new place was a land of planting seeds and reaping the harvest, and a new beginning for Israel. No longer are they whining children complaining as they wander the wilderness, being hand-fed by daily food from Heaven; now they would be mature followers of Jehovah, with purpose and permanence. Their food would be available because they cultivated the land, planted the seeds, gathered the harvest, and prepared the meals.

Consider what mindset you have about food.

One is to flit from diet gimmick to diet gimmick trying to find the shortcut that will magically take the pounds off quickly. Advertisements, Internet programs, and flash videos on social media entice us to try these alluring schemes. Maybe even joining First Place for Health was your attempt at finding a cure-all hack to solve your weight or health issues. This mindset is wilderness thinking. *Just feed me manna and fix me.*

Promised Land thinking is different — believing all food is given by God as an abundant and wonderful blessing. He has given me the tools through FP4H for healthy eating. We have amazing grocery stores and markets to buy fresh, colorful, healthy food. We are free to eat from the bounty of the harvest.

This Promised Land mindset comes from a mature understanding of the relationship God desires with us. Yes, He could spoon-feed us and plug us in like robots, and we would have no choice but to depend on Him. But He knows true happiness comes from trust-plus-obedience.

My food intake is a direct reflection of my relationship with God. The moment we place our trust in Jesus Christ and accept Him as our Savior, the Holy Spirit indwells us and seals us. Our body is His home, bought and paid for by the unblemished blood of Jesus Christ (1 Peter 1:18-19).

Instead of home, residence, or house, the Apostle Paul used a different word to describe our body in 1 Corinthians 6:19-20. How did he describe it in relationship with the Holy Spirit?

_____

_____

What do you think is the difference between a house and a temple?

_____

_____

_____

Our body is not only where the Holy Spirit lives; it is the sacred place where the Holy Spirit is to be revered, honored, and heard. When we are fully aware of the indwelling of the Spirit, we won't abuse our bodies with harmful substances. Neither will we overfeed or underfeed them. We will "walk by the Spirit, and … not gratify the desires of the flesh" (Galatians 5:16).

Read 1 Peter 1:14. What does Peter say about obedience?

_____

_____

What did Jesus say about obedience in Luke 6:46-47?

_____

_____

Here are some practical ways to make your body a temple worthy of the Holy Spirit. Beside each one, write what you will do to implement it.

Avoid unhealthy food temptations.

_____

_____

_____

Take time to rest and refresh.

_____

_____

_____

Exercise and develop strength.

_____

_____

_____

Lord, I need a new vision of my body — to see it as the temple of Your Holy Spirit. Open my eyes and my heart to make my body a sacred place where I do no harm.

⎯⎯ DAY 2: THE FASTED LIFE
Lord, help me feed on You. Give me strength and discernment.

I remember my first attempt at fasting. I had been challenged to consider this discipline by a pastor who explained the spiritual power and breakthrough it can bring. I read several books on fasting and found some guidelines, so one morning I embarked on my first fast. I got up early, and impulsively prayed an extra-long time before I left for work. At the office I resisted the breakfast offerings in the break room, and happily spent my lunch hour reading my Bible. Around 3:00 I began to feel weak and a bit faint, so I headed for the vending machines in the lobby. By the time I got home, I had eaten everything in sight and I was disgusted with myself. I couldn't even make it one day.

I read more books and articles on successful fasting and discovered it was not only a mental decision — I should have prepared my heart with prayer and Bible reading. I should have prepared my body by not rushing into the fast, and by eating small meals, especially raw fruits and vegetables, for a few days before I began. So I tried again, this time preparing mentally, spiritually, and physically, and I successfully fasted for 21 days. The spiritual impact of those days is still being measured in my life. Since then, there have been only a few seasons when I felt God calling me to fast again for a specific period of time.

In her book, "Truly Fed," Gari Meacham writes:

> "We have the wisdom and ability to listen to our stomachs and resist food when we've had enough. We tend not to believe this, though, because for years we've let diets, food programs, pills, doctors, and magazines tell us what to do. When learning about our hungry/full mechanism, one thing is for sure: with some practice and awareness, we can pinpoint the exact sensation of having enough and walk away feeling satisfied."

I asked Gari about living without food as my crutch. She told me about the power of living a "fasted life." I had never heard that terminology before, so I did some research and discovered that a fasted lifestyle is different from a long period of fasting.

A fasted lifestyle means not eating all you want but eating what you need.
Unfortunately, I've lived by a different mantra: Yum, this is good; can I have another helping? The Bible is clear about overeating and gluttony. Read these verses and write what God says.

Proverbs 23:20

_____

_____

Proverbs 23:2

_____

_____

1 Corinthians 6:12

_____

_____

Proverbs 25:27

_____

_____

1 Corinthians 8:13

_____

_____

Food was made for us — not us for food. God is clearly calling us to obey Him in living a life where we are in control of the food we eat, rather than living by craving or impulse.

Write a prayer asking God to help you begin living a fasted lifestyle regarding food.

_____

_____

_____

Food is the most obvious area where we can implement the fasted lifestyle, but other places may also need some pruning and shaping.

Shopping: How can you achieve a fasted lifestyle in your purchases of clothes, shoes, accessories, etc?

_____

_____

_____

Credit Card Debt: What steps can you take so the balances on your credit cards reflect your fasted lifestyle?

Relationships: What fasted lifestyle changes can you implement to build accord, affection, harmony, understanding, and friendship with acquaintances and relatives?

_____

_____

_____

Talking Too Much: My mentor once said she noticed that sometimes when she was talking with a group, an interruption would occur — a waiter taking an order, a phone ringing, etc. — but as soon as it was over she went back to her story (usually too long, with too much detail). One day she made a private rule for herself: if she was saying something and there was an interruption, she would keep quiet unless someone specifically asked her to restart or finish.

How can you improve your communication with others by fasting your urge to talk too much?

_____

_____

_____

Living a fasted lifestyle helps put your flesh under subjection and allows your faith to grow. God shows us in Isaiah 58:6-9 the power of living a fasted life. Controlling our urges to eat or drink or shop or talk too much breaks the power of sin. Failure to control our flesh and our urges opens doors for Satan to work. Choose a line from this passage and rewrite it with a message to yourself about living a fasted lifestyle.

_____

_____

_____

Lord, my heart is heavy with feelings of failure in the areas of overeating, over-talking, over-spending, overdoing. Lead me to a fasted lifestyle one step at a time.

Note: Fasting can have great spiritual power in your prayer life and your ability to obey God and overcome strongholds. But only God calls a person to this discipline. You should not decide to fast because someone else has tried it. Instead, hear God's voice before you make such a decision.

—— DAY 3: THE OBEDIENCE ATTITUDE

Lord, I confess my attitude needs a fix. Please help me change my mind and not use the world as a guide.

When I lost my job after more than 30 years climbing the corporate ladder, I faced a pivotal moment in my life story. Who was I now since I was no longer "Corporate Karen?" What would be the legacy I left on my world? I had choices. I could wallow in the pain and rejection wrapped up in the downsizing and ultimate elimination of my company. Or I could jump back into the industry with a different company and build on my reputation and strengths.

I'll admit the first option was tempting. I wanted everyone to feel sorry for me. Staggering in self-pity felt like the easiest step. The second option appealed to me as well because of the revenge factor: I'd show them they made a big mistake. But I also had a third option: I could use this moment to transition from a life lived to make a name for myself to a life that counted for the Lord. The rest of my life depended on my attitude and my choices.

Jesus spent 40 days in the wilderness fasting and praying. Mark Batterson says in "Draw the Circle: The 40 Day Prayer Challenge" that they "were a critical chapter in His life — the transition from His earthly father's business to His heavenly Father's business."

Satan stood aside watching and eventually tempting the Lord to follow His human nature for fame, food, and power, but Jesus chose the power of God, the fame of God's Name, and the food of the Word instead.

In Matthew 4, Jesus resisted Satan by using the Word of God as a sword against temptation. Here's my paraphrase: Satan asks, "Aren't you hungry?" Jesus replies, "It is written, man shall not live by bread alone." Stunned by the power of the Word, Satan tries another tactic. "So you want to live by Scripture, how about this one?" He quotes Psalm 91:11-12, tempting Jesus to jump from the highest point of the temple. "If you really believe Scripture, then jump." Jesus again responds with the Word and with obedience: "I will not tempt God. I will not put myself into a bad situation and expect a miracle." Instead, He obeyed the Father by sending the devil away.

After this encounter, Jesus preached to a crowd on a mountainside. Ministry often follows obedience. In this sermon, which we call the Sermon on the Mount, Jesus showed us how our attitude is the key to choosing the abundant life He offers.

Righteousness can't be measured by obeying rules or even by praying, fasting, or giving. Instead, righteousness begins in your heart, with your attitude. Then obedience, prayer, fasting, giving, etc., flow out of your heart.

In Matthew 5, Jesus presents attitudes that will help us make the choices He desires for us:

vs. 3. What should my attitude be about myself?

_____

_____

vv. 4-6. What should my attitude be about my sin?

_____

_____

vv. 7-9. What should my attitude be about my Lord?

_____

_____

vv. 10-16. What should my attitude be about my world?

_____

_____

When our attitude reflects our need for Him, our desire for righteousness and purity, and our love for others, we are radically changed as believers because we not only trust, but we obey and live a life of focus on Jesus. This new mindset is radically different from the world and worldviews around us.

Extraordinary acts of God begin with extraordinary acts of obedience. My life isn't about surviving or managing my sin or behaving like a good little Christian girl. As I grow in Christ, it is time to step out to obey and give all the glory to God. As I give my health and wellness to Christ, I must not focus on living with temptations I can't seem to shake. Instead, I must honor God with my eating and exercise and bring glory to Him in the temple where He resides.

Your calling is great, and the stakes are high. Don't settle into "survivor mode." Instead, determine to live a life of unexpected and stunning obedience.

Write a prayer asking God to help you live with an obedient attitude.

_____
_____
_____
_____

Lord, please help me see beyond the news and the wisdom of this world to the richer attitude of living in Your presence and outlook.

—— DAY 4: RAHAB'S FAITH AND OBEDIENCE

Lord, today I want to put my faith into action by obeying You even if it doesn't seem to make sense.

The J.B. Phillips paraphrase of the New Testament (Hebrews 11:30-31) uses the word "reconnoitre" to refer back to what the two Israelite spies were sent to do in Joshua 2. The term means to examine, explore, or probe. These men scouted the city to discover Jericho's strengths and weaknesses — information Joshua needed to form a battle plan. The two spies went to Rahab's house, which probably didn't draw much notice because she was a harlot and it is likely many male visitors ended up there when visiting Jericho.

But despite outward appearances, God's Spirit had been in Rahab's home before the spies arrived. Many visitors had brought rumors about God's dealings with Israel, and her heart was stirred through stories of victory over other people-groups and over nature (the Red Sea and Jordan River). A small flame of faith grew because she believed in the God of the rumors. She believed Jehovah was her salvation.

Rahab was an imperfect person by our standards and by the standards of God's Word, but God uses flawed people to accomplish His will, and He calls unsuitable people to trust in Him.

Read Joshua 2:9-11. What did Rahab say she knows about God?

_____
_____
_____

Rahab had fears but she believed in the God of Israel who had protected the nation.

Joshua 2 notes four characteristics of Rahab's faith. What does the Bible say about each one?

1) Fear of God _____

2) Bold not timid _____

3) Exhibits kindness_____

4) Takes action _____

The Canaanite religions didn't practice sexual purity. In fact, sexual acts may have been part of their worship experiences. Rahab may not have been an outcast, as we might think of a harlot in our culture. She may have been a businesswoman, an entrepreneur — some scholars think she may have had a business making linen thread because she had access to a scarlet rope for the spies. But outcast or not, she was an improbable person to protect and rescue them.

God used such an unlikely person because of her faith; she was spared from the destruction of the city.

Read what Rahab said to the spies in Joshua 2:8-11. What caused her to believe Israel's God was the one true God?

_____

_____

_____

According to Joshua 2:2-7, what did Rahab do for the spies?

_____

_____

_____

Her actions could be considered treason against Jericho's king, and acts of faith for Israel's God. In verse 9 Rahab explained that because of what she had seen and heard, she believed God had given Israel the land. She declared in verse 11 that "the LORD your God is God in heaven above and on the earth below." In this declaration and in her actions, she risked her business and her life.

James 2:18-19 says what about faith and deeds?

_____

_____

_____

Actions put feet to our faith. Remember how the priests got their feet wet when crossing the Jordan River? It is the same principle as Rahab hiding the spies. When we act upon our faith — taking action, risking life, or fortune, or fame — we show our faith.

Read Joshua 2:12-15. What did Rahab want in return for saving the lives of the spies?

_____

_____

They agreed to save her household if she placed a scarlet cord in the window. The spies reported back to Joshua in verse 24, "The LORD has surely given the whole land into our hands; all the people are melting in fear because of us." When Israel invaded Jericho, Rahab and her family were rescued, and God blessed her for her faith and action.

Read Matthew 1:5-6. Rahab married Salmon and together they had a son named _____ (vs. 5), who was the father of Obed, who had a son named Jesse, the father of King_____ (vs. 6). Rahab is the great-great-great-grandmother of King David and in the ancestry of Jesus Christ.

God honored her obedience and faith. He uses flawed people like you and me to accomplish His good purposes.

According to Hebrews 11:31, Rahab's faith was strong. She believed. What does James 2:25 say about it?

_____

_____

She had faith and she acted. God honors our faith when it's coupled with obedience — what The Message calls in the same verse "that seamless unity of believing and doing." What do you think this means?

_____

_____

_____

James 2:23-25 says Rahab was "credited" (also called "imputed") with righteousness because of her faith. Don't get confused and think your salvation — that moment when God counts you as righteous because of your faith in Jesus — somehow also requires you to do something to merit His salvation. When God counts us as righteous, it is on the basis of our faith in Jesus. He never looks to see if we already are righteous enough or good enough or if we behave in the right way.

No, He transfers the righteousness of Christ onto us and counts us as righteous. Theologically it is called "imputation" of righteousness, which means God sees me through a covering of Jesus' blood and sacrifice. I did nothing to deserve or earn it — it is because of my faith in Christ.

Nevertheless, my faith is proven by my actions.

What can you do this week to prove your faith in God?

_____

_____

_____

Lord, I believe You want me to add action to my faith. Show me the opportunities that come up today.

—— DAY 5: THE BLESSINGS OF FAITH AND OBEDIENCE

Lord, I believe You. I put all my trust in You whether I can see what You are doing or not.

In "Be Strong," Warren Wiersbe uses three words to describe Rahab's faith: courage, confidence, and concern.

Faith Takes Courage

Rahab believed in God before the spies arrived in Jericho because she had heard of His power in protecting His people from enemies, and His power over nature. Her faith gave her the courage to defy the king of Jericho and perhaps put her life in jeopardy, yet she trusted God for her rescue.

Read 1 Thessalonians 1:9. How did the people in Thessalonica show courage in their faith?

_____

_____

_____

Read 2 Kings 17:33. How did the people of Samaria fail in the courage of faith?

_____

_____

_____

Faith Takes Confidence

When I hear on the news about a person who accomplished some feat or overcame some adversity I often hear, "Well, I just had faith and made it through." Too often they don't tell in what or whom they had faith ... faith in faith, or faith in God, or faith in something else? Faith needs an object. Our faith is built on the all-powerful and all-authoritative God of the Universe. No other object of faith is worthy of our trust.

Rahab knew Israel's God was the true God because she had heard of His great power and wonders — that's confidence. She trusted Him to rescue her personally — that's faith. She helped the spies escape — that's faith in action.

Read in Joshua 2:9 about Rahab's confidence. What does Romans 10:17 say about this kind of faith?

_____

_____

_____

How are the promises of Exodus 15:14-16 and Deuteronomy 2:25 fulfilled in Rahab's faith?

_____

_____

_____

When has your faith exhibited confidence in the Lord?

_____

_____

_____

Joining First Place for Health and making the four-sided commitment to change your life physically, mentally, emotionally, and spiritually took confidence. What did you believe that helped you take the step to join FP4H?

_____

_____

_____

Faith Produces Concern

Rahab's faith led her to be concerned about her safety, and she was afraid for her family. Scripture is full of examples of people who brought others to Christ after they had discovered the Messiah.

In John 1:40-41, with whom did Andrew share the Good News?

_____

_____

In Mark 1:40-45, what did the cleansed leper do?

_____

_____

When has your faith exhibited concern for others?

_____

_____

_____

Joining First Place for Health also should produce concern for others. Write the name of a person you believe would benefit from joining FP4H, and a prayer asking God to help you reach out to them.

_____

_____

_____

Rahab wanted a guarantee from the spies about her family's safety. They agreed, and fulfilled their promise when Jericho fell — she and her family were rescued.

Lord, faith in You comes from deep within because of the courage You instill in me. You give me confidence because I know You are in control. Grant me the strength to become obedient to You in every way.

—— DAY 6: REFLECTION AND APPLICATION

Lord, You are awesome and amazing. I worship You because You are the Almighty God of the Universe.

Awe

The key to Rahab's survival is found in two words in Psalm 128:1: fear and obedience. "Fear the Lord" is a common command in the Bible. But fear of God is not being afraid. Instead, it is holding God in awe because of His holiness and power. God is glorious, majestic, and holy. He is not to be taken lightly or frivolously. Here are some reasons to hold God in awe. What words/descriptions can you add?

Matchless power   Creator of all
Sustainer of all   Purity
Perfection   Blessing-giver

_____   _____

_____   _____

_____   _____

Write a prayer of adoration telling the Lord why you adore and admire Him.

_____

_____

_____

_____

_____

_____

Lord, please give me faith like Rahab and cause me to follow through on my faith by being obedient to Your Word.

—— DAY 7: REFLECTION AND APPLICATION

Lord, I've asked You for the strength to be obedient, but it is easy for me to doubt. Help me hear You and believe You.

Before you obey
Obedience doesn't come naturally to us. Obedience that pleases God has three prerequisites.

Hearing the voice of Jesus
You can only hear His voice if you belong to Him by having accepted Him as your Savior. Then you can hear His prompting in your spirit. You may not hear Him audibly — not many do hear with their human ears. The voice of Jesus is heard most often with "spiritual ears." His voice is sweet and kind, and what He says always lines up perfectly with Scripture.

Believing what you've heard about Jesus
Rahab heard the rumors. She did not brush them off as mere gossip — she believed. When you hear someone testify about the goodness or power of God, pay attention. He may be feeding you information to help grow your faith.

Knowing God's will
Obedience is the key to knowing God's will for your life. When we fully surrender to His power and follow Him, He shows us the path to abundance and blessing.

What have you heard Jesus say about your health, and how can you be obedient to His voice?

_____
_____
_____

Lord, knowing Your will is my utmost desire.

WEEK SIX: STRENGTH WILL RISE BECAUSE … I FOLLOW

SCRIPTURE MEMORY VERSE
I have chosen the way of faithfulness; I have set my heart on your laws. Psalm 119:30

Joshua 3 and 4 show us how faith works when people join together to believe God. The troubles of the wilderness are behind them and God is calling the nation of Israel to victory and triumph. Victory comes from God, and we avail ourselves of victory by exercising our faith.

We are finally at that moment in the story of Joshua that Moses talked about in Deuteronomy 6:23: "But he brought us out … to bring us in … ." God rescued Israel from Egypt to take them to the Promised Land. Even though they detoured in the wilderness for 40 years, His plan was the same.

God has a purpose and a plan for each life He saves.

So far, we have tried to understand how the attitudes and choices we make affect our faith and obedience. Now we are poised for battle — fully equipped — stronger — soldiers ready to advance and possess the land.

As I write, we are in the middle of a worldwide pandemic. We have been isolated from each other for months, and everyone is anxious to get free from restriction. This morning I heard a preacher say we shouldn't be hoping to go back to normal, but anticipating going forward to normal.

We aren't built to go back or retreat or look backward. God calls us onward. But moving forward isn't for the faint of heart. Advancing to the future can produce anxiety. Change can create panic. Israel had felt this dread before when they said they should "choose a leader and go back to Egypt" (Numbers 14:4). The nation had rebelled when two of the first group of spies came back saying, "We should go up and take possession of the land, for we can certainly do it" (13:30). They were unwilling to take the steps of faith necessary to follow God into the Promised Land, and accepted the bad report from the 10 other spies instead.

But the next generation is ready to move forward. Consider how the Lord prepared them for the battle of Jericho:

- After years of wandering, they found a new vision for God's promises.
- God led them into the Jordan River, which He dried up so they could cross safely.
- They built a memorial to worship God and remember His miracles.
- They made a vow and sealed it with the rite of circumcision.
- They rested and healed and sought God.
- Joshua met the Lord in a personal encounter.
- Israel celebrated Passover.
- They tasted new food and discovered new obedience.

As you review this list, reflect on your life, your situation, and your heart. Contemplate how God has spoken to you so far in this study and how He has given you a new mind-set, attitude, or desire. What has He taught you about your health and wellness?

_____

_____

_____

Write a prayer thanking Him for the joy of knowing He is at work, and for the anticipation of what is to come.

_____

_____

_____

—— DAY 1: WALLS

Lord, my problems seem like walled cities that are impenetrable. I have no hope of victory unless You step in. Help me see behind the walls with Your eyes.

According to Joshua 6:1, the "gates of Jericho were securely barred because of the Israelites. No one went out and no one came in."

Archeologists believe Jericho was one of the earliest settlements in history, and may have been one of the first to have a wall. In fact, by the time Israel crossed the Jordan River, the city had two walls made of mud-brick and stone. Experts estimate the outside wall had a stone base about 15 feet high, with a 26-foot brick wall about six feet thick built on top. The inside wall was some 46 feet above ground-level.

The residents of Jericho built walls around the city just as we build barriers around ourselves. You may have begun construction on your walls in childhood, if you grew up in an environment where it wasn't safe to express your feelings or where it was safer to avoid conflict. You may have built walls as a teenager when you didn't fit with the "in" crowd, or as an adult when life seemed out of control. Walls help us feel power over what may happen next.

Let's explore some basic walls and ask God to help us discover why we build them.

Walls to Protect
When my children were small, I developed a friendship with a wonderful, talented woman who loved the Lord deeply and believed in me unconditionally. We shared our lives, our parenting dilemmas, our service at church, our hearts. We connected on every level. But one day she came to my house with accusations and attacks that ranged from my terrible personality to my kids' behavior. I was stunned at what she said, especially the vitriol with which she said it. I responded by building a wall so nothing like that would happen again. I refused to get close to any other woman for years.

We build walls to protect ourselves from pain — to keep out hurtful elements, enemies, and friends who wound. But as author and speaker Susan Jeffers said, "The wall that protects you, also imprisons you." Walls keep us hemmed in. We keep our bad feelings nearby and we are not free.

Proverbs 18:1 says, "An unfriendly (*isolated*) person pursues selfish ends and against all sound judgment starts quarrels" (italics mine).

Have you built a wall of protection around yourself? What prison does this wall also contain?

_____

_____

_____

Walls to Impress
There was a time when the buzz-word of women in business was, "Dress to impress." It encouraged women to maintain a professional image in the workplace to help them be taken seriously. One idea was to dress for the position you wanted, not the job you were doing. I'm glad women are being hired more for their expertise and

skills these days than how they look. Even so, there's a lot of good advice out there for dressing appropriately and making a great impression.

I once hired an executive assistant who seemed confident and put-together, with a professional appearance at the interview. The next Monday, a messy, disordered woman tapped at my door, and I asked if I could help her. She said she was here to start her new job. I didn't recognize her from the week before. She couldn't have looked more different. She had impressed me at first, but the "real" person let me down.

We want to influence others, but a false wall built to impress is dangerous. 1 Samuel 16:7 says, "But the LORD said to Samuel, 'Do not consider his appearance or his height, for I have rejected him. The LORD does not look at the things people look at. People look at the outward appearance, but the LORD looks at the heart.'"

What walls to impress have you erected? What prisons do the walls contain?

Walls of Identification

I built a wall labeled, "Corporate Karen," when I was an executive. Every word I said, every activity I participated in, every outfit I wore was premeditated to reflect the image I wanted to portray. No stranger, and few close friends, could get behind that wall to see the real me.

We build a facade to protect ourselves or to project an image. Some walls are negative and push people away: *I am an alcoholic. I am fat. I am nothing. I can't. I'm just a* _____. You fill in the blank. Some walls are pretentious, using fancy words or name-dropping. Some walls are pompous, to make us sound smart.

The Bible says we don't need to portray an identity because our unique personality is found in Christ.

> "For we are God's handiwork, created in Christ Jesus to do good works, which God prepared in advance for us to do" (Ephesians 2:10).
> " ... and to put on the new self, created to be like God in true righteousness and holiness" (Ephesians 4:24).

WEEK SIX   STRENGTH WILL RISE BECAUSE...I FOLLOW

What walls of identity have you erected? What prisons do the walls contain?

_____

_____

_____

Living life behind walls can bring rejection, criticism, destruction, hurting, controlling, and "keeping score." Living wall-free allows us to pursue our dreams in freedom, using our talents and abilities to the fullest.

Lord, I don't want to live behind a wall I have created thinking I am protecting myself. Instead, help me tear down the false and pretentious walls so I can follow You completely.

—— DAY 2: THE WALLS OF JERICHO
Lord, I want to know the end from the beginning, but I am learning that giving You control and following You regardless are better than my need to understand.

Israel was ready to take the Promised Land. The first big city was Jericho, with thick walls and a fierce battle-force. In Joshua 6:2-5, God tells Joshua the strange plan for conquering the city. Read through these verses and list every instruction.

_____

_____

_____

To a military commander, these must have seemed peculiar. Joshua may have wondered how they would use their military skills and equipment. If he'd been planning the attack, he would have come up with some fighting strategies. But Joshua had learned to trust God, so he proceeded with God's plan.

Read Joshua 6:6-7 and list all the instructions Joshua gave the people.

_____

_____

_____

What instructions and descriptions did he leave out?

_____

_____

_____

Joshua told the people to march around the city, but he didn't tell them the entire plan. He said to follow the Ark of the Covenant; they didn't know it was going to be for seven days. They weren't told that a mighty shout on the seventh day would cause the walls to fall. They were told only to march.

I can imagine the confusion, bewilderment, and sarcasm: "We're just marching?" "We're not fighting?" "Why can't we say a word?" "This plan isn't working." Then the next day: "Just walking. Just marching. No fighting. No battle. Just walking."

Read Joshua 6:14. What do you think was going through the minds of these warriors on the sixth day?

In Psalm 13:1-2 David wrote, "How long, LORD?" Have you asked God how much longer you will have to go through what you are facing? I have. Sometimes I think, *If God would just tell me how many laps I have to take, I could make it to the end.* But God doesn't want us to obey from our knowledge. Obedience calls us to march whether or not we know if the walls will fall. I've learned that even if they don't come down, I will be changed in the process of marching. When you keep marching, God will change you too.

What are your walls made of?
- Food
- Health
- Family
- Finances
- Unforgiveness
- Anxiety
- Anger

For years I carried a grudge against someone who had manipulated a work situation. I felt justified. I complained about prejudice against women. I hated that he seemed to have an inside connection I couldn't grasp because he was male. I was convinced I was more qualified, and sure I had worked harder. Yet he was promoted and I was left behind. I allowed resentment to become a wall between me and this person and between me and our superiors.

WEEK SIX   STRENGTH WILL RISE BECAUSE...I FOLLOW

One day I was reading in The Message and the words of 2 Corinthians 10:3-5 caused me to pause. I realized the wall of resentment was making my life miserable, affecting my work, and undermining any future chances I had of being promoted.

Here is the passage:

"The world is unprincipled. It's dog-eat-dog out there. The world doesn't fight fair. But we don't live or fight our battles that way — never have and never will. The tools of our trade aren't for marketing or manipulation, but they are for demolishing that entire massively corrupt culture."

What phrases show you what to do about walls that need to come down?

_____

_____

_____

Tearing down my wall meant I had to trust God to make my way — even though I couldn't see the future. Destroying the bitterness and rancor in my heart forced me to make amends with my co-worker, and weed out feelings of rejection and unfairness in my heart.

Write a few sentences about a wall you've built. How did you build it and what have you tried to tear it down, only to fail?

_____

_____

_____

Some of your walls may have been there forever, or it feels like forever. God wants to tear them down. He never asked you to get a bulldozer and do it yourself — He only asks that you keep walking. I know it doesn't make sense, but keep walking. What if you are on the sixth lap? Is victory just around the next corner? Will you keep walking?

Write a prayer committing to walk with Jesus even when you don't know the future.

_____

_____

_____

Lord, I am willing to keep walking and walking when I can't see the path. I am counting on You to do as the children's song says: "make the walls come tumbling down."

—— DAY 3: NO REBUILDING ALLOWED

Lord, I thank You for tearing down my strongholds. I am free and ready to serve You. I never want to go back to the fear and anxiety of walls.

When the battle of Jericho was over, Joshua pronounced a curse on anyone who tried to rebuild the walls (Joshua 6:26-27). The fortress was the first to fall in Israel's conquest of Canaan. Read Joshua 6:17-19. Notice the declarations he makes about Jericho:

vs. 17. The city and all that is in it are to be _____

vs. 18. But keep away from the _____ things

vs. 19. All the silver and gold and the articles of bronze and iron are _____ _____ to the Lord

The miracle of the battle was clear: God caused the walls to fall. He was the conqueror and everything in Jericho belonged to Him. The stronghold was destroyed, and Joshua cursed any builder who tried to reconstruct the fortification walls. The curse was not on rebuilding the city, or on any people who would later inhabit it — it specifically was placed on the builder.

Read 1 Kings 16:34. What does it reveal about the man named Hiel who tried to rebuild Jericho in the time of King Ahab?

_____

_____

_____

We have seen how Jericho represents strongholds in various areas of our lives. We set up walls to separate us from pain; we build barriers that stifle our future. But when God has given us victory over strongholds, we must never build them again. What does 1 Corinthians 15:57 say about victory?

_____

_____

Jesus won our battles on the cross. We don't have to fight the same ones again and again. No matter what our strongholds have been or how hard we have had to fight, God has broken down the walls and we are free. How does Paul phrase this freedom in Romans 8:1?

_____

_____

Food Strongholds

I can testify that the fortified stronghold of sweets was a Jericho in my life, especially if the sweet was creamy and cold. But because First Place for Health helped me face the walls I'd built around my cravings for sweets, I have lost those desires. The walls were built of secrecy (if no one sees me eat it, the calories don't count) and developed from defiance (I deserve this treat, and no one can tell me what to do). Yet in His mercy, God reached down and lifted me out of the pit so now I no longer am a slave to sweets. I never want to go back to that addiction.

What food strongholds have you overcome?

_____

_____

_____

Family Strongholds

I know someone who hadn't spoken to his family in years. Long-ago hurtful words and actions were walls as big as Jericho in his heart. One day his sister called asking forgiveness and begging him to attend a family event. He knew God wanted him to tear down those walls, so he went home. Today he is still waiting for all the walls to fall, but he feels the joy of broken strongholds, and vows never to turn back in his family relationships.

What family strongholds have you overcome?

_____

_____

_____

Financial Strongholds

Perhaps in the past you have lived with credit card debt, high-interest loans, or purchases beyond your means. You know the strangulation and pressure of never enough money to go around.

What financial strongholds have you overcome?

_____

_____

_____

Just as the people of Israel kept walking day after day around Jericho while they waited on God to destroy the stronghold, you and I must be vigilant about never allowing those walls to be rebuilt. God will help us. We don't have to keep fighting the same battles over and over.

Here are some tools to help you keep the walls of your strongholds down. Circle what you think will help you never rebuild a Jericho in your life.

No sweets	No fried foods
More fruits	More vegetables
Go to the gym	Commit to Bible study
Help someone else	Speak kind words
Seek God's will	Don't take offense at someone's words
Pray	Learn a new skill
No compulsive shopping	Forgive

Choose one of these tools. How will you implement the new idea this week?

_____

_____

_____

Lord, with Your help, I will never rebuild the Jerichos in my life. I need Your constant touch on my heart and mind, reminding me of the terror of strongholds and the freedom of victory.

—— DAY 4: ORDER MY STEPS

Lord, I commit my steps to You. Please direct me to the path You have chosen for me. Reveal the inexplicable joy and easy contentment that happen when I am following Your will and purpose.

There are days when I think I should retire. Sounds good, doesn't it? Give up work, take a nap, do what I want to do instead of what I'm responsible for. But what if it's not over yet? What if the best is yet to come?

The best is not behind you, and God isn't finished.

In a classic cartoon, two characters are shooting arrows toward targets and missing not only the bullseye but the entire target. In the final frame one says, "Here's the way you do it," and the drawing shows that he shoots the arrow first, then draws the bullseye and target around it.

Too often we live like that cartoon character. We rock along, never going for the big thing God has planned, because of circumstances and problems and setbacks. And we settle for a target we drew after we shot the arrow. It can happen in our spiritual life and in our quest for wellness.

What does Psalm 37:23-24 say about how God orders our steps? What assurance does this give you?

_____

_____

_____

God has an "on purpose" for you and me. His plans for you are good. He knows what you've been through, the wildernesses you've wandered, the battles you've fought. He sees how your heart longs to obey Him. He has a plan for you.

We've read the promise in Jeremiah 29 that says He has a plan for our good, and in Romans 8:28 that says all things work together for good. We know the Bible characters — Moses, Noah, Ruth, Deborah, David, Paul, Peter — God chose for great accomplishments. But God's plans for us are personal and apply to us uniquely. The questions we need to answer are: *Do I believe God has a plan for me? How hard will I work to discover that plan and follow it?*

How does Psalm 32:8 encourage you in the search for God's purpose for your life?

_____

_____

_____

How does it encourage you in your wellness journey to lose weight and get strong?

_____

_____

_____

My husband and I are on a quest to visit all the presidential libraries; there are 13 in the US library system. We have visited 12, finding time when we travel across the country, and we hope to visit the last one this year. The libraries are from New York to California, typically in the hometown of the President. The pursuit to visit them has been a kind of "bucket list" for us. Friends have made other bucket lists such as visiting all the national parks or all the Major League Baseball stadiums. Bucket lists are fun because we set a goal and keep trying until we reach it.

Some of our bucket lists require intervention from God because only He can make them happen. Sometimes following God wholly and fully requires us to believe Him for something that is so big, He *has* to show up.

What *so big* item is on your First Place for Health bucket list?

_____

_____

_____

What *so big* item is on your spiritual bucket list?

_____

_____

_____

Lord, I don't want to make a move until You order my steps, but I also don't want to sit still. Help me dream big and depend on You for success.

—— DAY 5: FOLLOWING IN SPITE OF SELF

Lord, love of self is my biggest wall to break down. I admit I am always ready to pro-tect myself, and to satisfy my selfish desires and promote myself. Change my focus from self to a view of all You have planned for my life.

Imagine the thoughts of the people walking around the walls of Jericho for seven days. The desert air was hot and unpleasant. The people of the city mocked from the top of the walls every day, making each step of the two-mile hike miserable. And the plan didn't seem to be working — they kept walking with no results. The whole exercise was tedious and tiresome.

It is our nature to rebel against God and promote ourselves, as Paul warns in 2 Timothy 3:2-4. What does he say we might become?

_____

_____

Read Romans 7:14-25. It shows how Paul, the great apostle, fought the battle with self. What phrase or phrases stand out?

_____

_____

The battle with self is the battle with feelings of "what I want." My mind says, "I want to be healthy, happy, and full." How is that mentality detrimental to our wellness journey?

_____

_____

_____

Because of my self-love, I might have been impatient with Joshua and his plan to walk. I might have thought about the pleasant fields back at camp or dreamed of reclining in my tent, keeping cool. I might have wondered why we weren't using the traditional tools of war like battering rams, ladders, clubs, and catapults.

We face walls of self-love, which may be built of character weaknesses or spiritual blindness, and we fall into self-idolatry with possessions, fame, or success. We want immediate results and solutions.

Read 2 Corinthians 10:3-4. How does Paul describe our weapons?

They are not:

_____

They are designed to bring down:

_____

They are for taking captive every:

_____

On the last day when Joshua told the marchers to shout, I might have started half-heartedly, thinking it was more of the same nonsense. But as the shout of perhaps 2 million people began to come together in one mighty sound, and the walls cracked, then crumbled, then tumbled, I might have shouted louder and more enthusiastically. Jericho didn't fall in one day. It took 13 trips around the walls. How close I might have come to allowing my selfish nature to turn away from following God's plan. What do you think would have happened if the people stopped walking?

Read Proverbs 14:12 and Isaiah 55:8 to help you answer.

_____

_____

According to Joshua 5:1, what had God said about the end result of the battle?

_____

_____

God did it because He is stronger and more powerful than our skills or our thoughts.

Imagine Rahab during those seven days, and the questions in her mind. Will I be rescued? *Will I be arrested for treason? Will my family stay in the house as we wait to be spared?* The fear must have been great. Archeologists have discovered that the walls crumbled except in one corner. I believe this was Rahab's house. She and her family were rescued. Researchers have found evidence of earthquake activity at the time the city met its end. If God used an earthquake to accomplish His purposes that day, it was still a miracle since it happened at precisely the right moment and somehow protected Rahab's house. No matter what agency God used, it was ultimately He who brought the walls down.

What does Hebrews 11:30 say brought them down?

_____

Lord, I want to follow You by knocking down the walls of self. But I often don't recognize the self-love, self-promotion, and self-protection that lurk within me. Please reveal my self-idolatry and make me strong enough to bring those walls down with Your help.

—— DAY 6: REFLECTION AND APPLICATION
Lord, breaking down walls is hard work. Please help me.

Breaking Walls
Many years ago, someone told me they had access to a wholesaler who would sell me a Rolex watch. I was excited because the price was much less than retail; in fact, it would only be $80. Cash. I was all in. The watch was pretty, but it wasn't long before it stopped working and I had to take it to a jeweler for repair. He asked, "Where did you get this?" I said, "From a guy." Of course, the watch was a fake.

Satan would love for you to believe a lie about the walls that keep you from victory. We must choose the truth and follow the Lord in every situation. Following God and breaking down walls is hard work, and we often don't know where God is leading. We want to turn our mistakes into successes and our failures into miracles, but we don't know how. Yet God is willing to bring us near.

Peter betrayed Jesus when he denied Him three times during His trial, yet Jesus restored and blessed him. Nothing you have ever done is so repulsive to God that He won't restore and redeem you. God is not out to get us — He is out to restore us. The question is, how close are you to Him today? If you have ever been closer than you are right now, you are living a counterfeit life and, like my watch, you will not function.

Spend the day considering your willingness to draw nearer to Him.

Lord, You said, "Draw near to Me and I will draw near to you." I need Your restoration and peace. Please expose my bogus feelings or attitudes and help me discover Your truth.

—— DAY 7: REFLECTION AND APPLICATION
Lord, I choose Your role in my life.

God's Role
Little league soccer is great for young children because it doesn't require a lot of hand-eye coordination and the rules are simple. The tiny players are encouraged to run as hard as they can. When my son played, neither he nor the other boys under- stood their roles at first. Wherever the ball went, they all ran. Of course this left the rest of the field and the goal open for some surprise action from the opposing team. But by the end of the season, each player had learned his position, and that he was to stay there and protect that area rather than run after the ball.

We too must learn our position and role, then we can place ourselves into God's hands. Most of us have misunderstood our role — we have confused it with God's role. He lives in us. "I have been crucified with Christ and I no longer live, but Christ lives in me" (Galatians 2:20a). He does the work in our lives that makes us into what He wants us to be. " ... being confident of this, that He who began a good work in you will carry it on to completion until the day of Christ Jesus" (Philippians 1:6).

We can trust God to give us victory. Much of our defeat comes because we so often quote Matthew 26:41b: "The spirit is willing, but the flesh is weak." It is true, but we use it like a crutch when we fail. We have forgotten that the Bible also says, " ... it is God who works in you ... " (Philippians 2:13).

Three statements are true about every believer:

1) We have been saved from the penalty of sin
2) We are being saved from the power of sin
3) We shall be saved from the presence of sin

First, the believer is not condemned (John 3:18) and is saved from God's wrath (Romans 5:9). Second, Jesus is able to keep us (Jude 24-25) and is faithful to protect us (2 Thessalonians 3:2-4). And third, we shall be like Him one day (1 John 3:2) and we will be completely transformed (Philippians 3:20-21).

Most Christians understand the first statement — we know we have been saved from the penalty of sin and that Jesus washed away our guilt. And we understand the third statement — we cling to the blessed hope that we will go to Heaven.

Our problem is that we don't fully believe the second statement. We don't comprehend that we are currently being saved from the power of sin. Our skepticism grows because we have felt the defeat of daily failures.

It's time to ask ourselves these questions: "Did Jesus die so I would only partially follow Him? Will I embrace absolute surrender, which is positive, unquestioning, and outright relinquishing my power and control to the power and control of God?" Absolute surrender is absolutely impossible — on our own.

All my life I have known that God had more for me; He intended to use me in some way. Yet I haven't lived like I believed it. I've made wrong choices and wrong decisions. When I've realized my mistakes, I've tried to shape up and get everything right again, but I rarely do. My best actions do not come close to the freedom and joy that come from God.

Today ponder the way you follow Christ. Is it in absolute or partial surrender?

Lord, I want to follow You in absolute surrender.

WEEK SEVEN: STRENGTH WILL RISE BECAUSE ... I REPENT

SCRIPTURE MEMORY VERSE
Direct my footsteps according to your word; let no sin rule over me. Psalm 119:133

From the Old Testament prophets to John the Baptist, and Jesus to the Apostles, we find hundreds of commands to repent. Perhaps no one said it more comprehensively than Isaiah:

> "Seek the LORD while he may be found; call on him while he is near. Let the wicked forsake their ways and the unrighteous their thoughts. Let them return to the LORD, and he will have mercy on them, and to our God, for he will freely pardon" (Isaiah 55:6-7).

God calls us to return to Him when we have strayed. According to Isaiah, returning requires us to seek God, forsaking our wicked ways and unrighteous thoughts. The Bible speaks about all of these.

Seeking God
"Look to the LORD and his strength; seek his face always" (1 Chronicles 16:11). "And without faith it is impossible to please God, because anyone who comes to him must believe that he exists and that he rewards those who earnestly seek him" (Hebrews 11:6).

Forsaking Our Wicked Ways
"Whoever conceals their sins does not prosper, but the one who confesses and renounces them finds mercy" (Proverbs 28:13).

"Therefore, since we are surrounded by such a great cloud of witnesses, let us throw off everything that hinders and the sin that so easily entangles. And let us run with perseverance the race marked out for us ... " (Hebrews 12:1).

Forsaking Our Unrighteous Thoughts
"We demolish arguments and every pretension that sets itself up against the knowledge of God, and we take captive every thought to make it obedient to Christ" (2 Corinthians 10:5).

"Finally, brothers and sisters, whatever is true, whatever is noble, whatever is right, whatever is pure, whatever is lovely, whatever is admirable — if anything is excellent or praiseworthy — think about such things" (Philippians 4:8).

—— DAY 1: THE BATTLE WITH PRIDE

Lord, pride wants its own way in my life. I know You alone are worthy to receive honor, glory, and praise. Please help me declare war on pride and the arrogance and self-promotion that come with it.

After the victory at Jericho, how was Joshua viewed in the eyes of the people, according to Joshua 6:27?

_____

From assistant to Moses to mighty warrior and extraordinary leader, Joshua proved himself to be a man who listened to God and obeyed the word of the Lord. His commission from God was clear — to take the land He had promised. Read Joshua 1:3 and write God's promise.

_____

_____

Like a good general, Joshua set his sights on the next conquest. According to Joshua 7:2-3, he sent spies to the next city, Ai. What was their report?

_____

_____

_____

It seemed to these spies that the little town of Ai would be easy pickings, especially after the stunning win at Jericho. Read Joshua 7:4-5 and describe the battle.

_____

_____

_____

How easy it can be to forget that all victories come from the Lord. We get cocky and proud and sure of ourselves. It wasn't wrong for Joshua to send spies. Proverbs 20:18 says, "Plans are established by seeking advice; so if you wage war, obtain guidance." Joshua's mistake was assuming the Lord was ready to move. We must seek God for every new challenge and not rely on past victories — no matter how recent or spectacular. From a human point of view — even a military point of view — the small city of Ai seemed nothing to worry about.

Look again at the spies' report in Joshua 7:3. Who is left out of the analysis?

_____

_____

_____

What does Proverbs 16:18 say about pride?

_____

_____

_____

Our personal battles are not our own.

I remember when I joined a First Place for Health class at my church. At that time there were two true facts about me: 1) I loved the Lord and depended on Him and 2) I had never thought of asking Him for help with my weight problem.

I suppose I thought He didn't have time for my constant battle with unhealthy food. Maybe He was too busy running the universe for me to bother Him with the quantity and quality of what I ate. I believed I had gotten myself into the overweight situation, and I would have to get myself out.

That year in First Place we went through the *Seek God First* Bible study. I wrote this quote from page 72 in my journal: "The key to making good decisions and right choices is to keep our eyes focused on Jesus and the Word of God."

That phrase made a huge impact on me. Every decision — not only choices I think are big or spiritual, about ministry or serving God — matters to the Lord. My choices of foods and calories and nutrition are just as important to Jesus as my decision to accept a position at church or witness to my neighbor or forgive someone who hurt me. In all areas of life, I please Him by keeping my eyes focused on Him.

Pride can keep me from hearing Jesus or seeing His work. Pride stems from self-importance and a feeling of superiority. Eighteenth-century American preacher Jonathan Edwards identified seven subtle signs, like symptoms of an illness, in his essay, *Undetected Spiritual Pride*.

The first sign is finding fault with others — I can see what is wrong with you much faster than I can see what's wrong in my life. The second is harshness — constantly being irritated by and belittling others. The third is pretense — caring more about what people think of us than we should. The fourth sign is the *everyone is against me* defensive posture. The fifth is leaving God out of our decisions. The sixth and seventh signs are being desperate for attention and neglecting others. All seven affect our sight, keeping us from focusing on Jesus.

When we pat ourselves on the back for how well we are doing, we need to cry out like David did in Psalm 139:23-24. Write those verses.

_____

_____

_____

Has God shown you any symptoms of pride lurking in your heart or actions? Write about it.

_____

_____

_____

Edwards went on to say: "The spiritually proud man thinks he is full of light already and feels that he does not need instruction, so he is ready to ignore the offer of it. On the other hand, the humble person is like a little child who easily receives instruction."

Read Psalm 25:9. What does God do for the humble?

_____

_____

"Nothing sets a Christian so much out of the devil's reach than humility and so prepares the mind for divine light." ~ Jonathan Edwards

Lord, I pray that I will come to such a relationship with You that when You speak, I will hear and respond. Correct my heart by helping me choose humility over pride. Open my eyes to the clarity humility brings.

—— DAY 2: THE BATTLE AT AI

Lord, I never want to go backward in my walk with You. I disobey too often and try to hide my sin from others and You. Please forgive me and help me start fresh with You each morning, keeping short accounts and an open heart.

Ai was in the hill country about 15 miles from Jericho. When the Israelites attacked they met fierce resistance, and the army of Ai chased them away. In the process, 36 of Israel's soldiers were killed.

Read Joshua 7:6. How did Joshua and the elders respond?

_____

_____

_____

Imagine Joshua's dilemma. He had been championed as the great leader (Joshua 6:27), and now he is at his lowest point. Our best plans often are ruined, and our dreams dashed, just when we least expect it. Joshua had not known defeat, but now he lay face down before God with dust heaped on his head.

Read Joshua 7:7. Who did he blame?

_____

Not only did Joshua seem to blame God for the defeat, he said it would have been better if they had stayed on the east side of the Jordan River and never entered the Promised Land. We say and think foolishly when we face defeat. Imagine if they had stayed there — they wouldn't have experienced the miracle of the drying up of the river, or worship and thanksgiving in building the memorial to God; nor would they have made the solemn commitment of circumcision or known the celebration of Passover. Not to mention the stunning intervention of God when the walls came down at Jericho. Oh, they would have missed a lot.

One defeat and Joshua wanted to go back. One defeat and unbelief made him content to settle for less than God's best. One defeat and he no longer trusted God. Looking back helps us see how far we have come, what obstacles God has removed, and what opportunities He has given us. But looking back should never lead us to want to go back.

If you went back before joining First Place for Health, what lessons or unexpected blessings would you miss?

_____

_____

_____

What does Hebrews 6:1 say about going back?

_____

_____

Read Joshua 7:10-12. What is God's response to Joshua?

_____

_____

_____

Israel should have easily conquered Ai. Read Joshua 7:1. Why did they lose the battle?

_____

_____

_____

What does Isaiah 59:2 warn about the consequences of sin?

_____

_____

In Joshua 7 God instructed the people to prepare for a serious and solemn assembly. Each tribe was brought forward, clan by clan, family by family, man by man, to search out the sin. God sifted the nation to find the tribe of Judah, the Zerahites, the clan of Zimri, and the family of Karmi, until finally the one man, Achan, was singled out.

The sin involved one man who had stolen from God and pretended he had obeyed the Lord. When Achan was confronted, he confessed. What did he say in Joshua 7:20-21?

_____

_____

_____

Achan saw a beautiful Babylonian robe and some silver and gold, and he couldn't resist. He took these because he wanted them so much. God had given specific instructions to Israel about not taking booty when they conquered Jericho, but this one man was enticed by desire and brought defeat to the nation. I've often wondered where Achan thought he was going to wear that robe. Imagine the comments: *Hey, Achan, where'd you get the new clothes? Rob a bank?*

The stolen goods were recovered from a hole he had dug in the family tent, which tells us the family was complicit. They were all put to death and burned, along with the booty — a dramatic warning to Israel to not take God's word lightly.

One man's sin affected an entire nation. In Joshua 7:15, Achan's actions are translated as "an outrageous thing in Israel." The root words indicate that his sin brought terrible shame on Israel by breaking the covenant and disobeying God. It is a dire warning to us about the influence we wield in our families, churches, communities, and nation. God does not view sin lightly.

Spend some time in prayer today asking the Lord to reveal your secret sins and give you the humility to ask forgiveness.

Lord, please reveal whatever is hidden. Search me. Know me. Find any wickedness in me. Shower grace on me so I will find Your forgiveness.

—— DAY 3: LET NO SIN RULE
Lord, You call us to be pure and clean. Forgive me for allowing sin to stain my heart. Help me take a new path of repentance and obedience.

Years ago in the South, churches planned summer revival meetings. Typically, a special speaker was invited to preach every morning and evening for a week. Church members invited townfolk, who came in large numbers. People who attended were convicted by the preaching of the Word, and filled the altars, crying buckets of tears because they were so sorry for their sins. Unfortunately for many, nothing changed, and they came back to the next summer's revival to cry over their sins again.

God calls us to more than feeling sorry for our sins; He calls us to repent. According to Matthew 4:17, repentance was Jesus' major message while He was on Earth. What does that verse say?

_____

_____

_____

It is time we learned the truth about repentance, because we can confuse it with tears or being sorry. Too often our sorrow for sin actually is sorrow that we got caught. Tears may flow when we repent, but tears are not required. We might confuse repentance with guilt, remorse, or regret. Let's consider the differences.

Guilt is feeling responsible for some crime or offense. Guilt is a prison with chains that will never let you go. Guilt is wallowing in feelings of shame.

Remorse is sorrow for the sin. Remorse can breed sadness, depression, and a hopeless feeling as you become a slave to the sorrow.

Regret is shame that focuses on me, my losses, my pain. Regret is overblown, self-indulgent pity that sees only my difficulties and hardships.

Do you think any of these reactions to sin meets the test of what God calls us to when He says repent? Why?

_____
_____
_____

The definition of "repent" is "to change." Repenting is making a decision and taking action to change your heart, your thought processes, your actions, and your feelings. Repenting is making a U-turn — turning around to go in the opposite direction. Guilt, remorse, and regret don't cause real change. When we discover part of our life that is on the wrong path, God calls us to repent. If we haven't changed, we haven't repented. Let's consider some important areas that might require change and true repentance.

Unforgiveness

The pain caused by someone's hurtful words or actions can sit on our heart and breed the anger and pain that fester when we refuse to forgive. When you hear the word "unforgiveness," is there a person or situation on your heart that needs attention? Write about it.

_____
_____
_____
_____
_____

In her book, "When He Leaves," Noelle Quinn says she found it very difficult to forgive her husband who left their marriage, so she determined to forgive him 1 percent at a time: "Each day I pray to forgive one-percent more."

How might this idea of forgiving a little at a time work for you? Remember, repentance is about change.

_____

_____

_____

Unhealthy Food Choices

No matter how many classes we attend or Bible studies we complete or trackers we fill out, nothing will change in our wellness until we repent of our old ways and turn in a new direction of food choices. What foods do you need to stop eating and what foods do you need to eat? What will you change?

_____

_____

_____

First Place for Health's COO, Lisa Lewis, recommends some food substitutions:
- Applesauce instead of oil, butter or sugar
- Nonfat Greek yogurt instead of mayo or sour cream
- Mashed bananas instead of sugar, butter, or fats
- Nuts for croutons in salads, or granola in yogurt
- Rolled oats for breadcrumbs
- Zucchini ribbons or spaghetti squash for pasta

How would implementing Lisa's changes help you make a U-turn in your wellness journey?

_____

_____

_____

David was the mighty king of Israel, yet he sinned grievously when he had an affair with Bathsheba and ordered the death of her husband. God sent the prophet Nathan to confront the king about his sin. David felt great sorrow and regret, but until he named and repented of his sin, he was in bondage to the pain of failure. He wrote Psalm 51 to express his deep sorrow and repentance. As you read David's words, write the phrases that touch you and explain why.

_____

_____

_____

Role of the Holy Spirit

Peter preached a powerful sermon recorded in the Book of Acts. What does Acts 2:37 say happened to the people who heard the message?

In Ephesians 6:17, Paul says the Word of God — which is what Peter preached that day (see also Joel 2, Psalm 16, Psalm 110) — is the sword of the Spirit — the Holy Spirit, the Spirit of Truth. That sword cut through the noise in their hearts and caused them to say, "What must I do?"

What is Peter's answer to their question (Acts 2:38)?

Repenting from sin, no matter the origin, is the key to living a full and abundant life.

Lord, please fill my heart and mind with the power of the Holy Spirit. Convict me by the power of Your Word. Help me turn around in repentance to follow Your way.

—— DAY 4: GOD IS HOLY

Lord, my human brain does not comprehend Your holiness, and it is not possible for me to attain Your purity. So I ask for Your supernatural power to instill holiness into my life.

No discussion about repentance would be complete without understanding the holiness of God.

The Hebrew word for holy — kadesh — means "separate," which describes how God is set apart from mankind because of His pure character and eternal nature. No hint of sin or evil can touch Him because He is perfect in every way. He is always right and always perfect.

Read Romans 3:23. How can we ever match God's holiness?

God's standard of holiness can never be accomplished by a human; we will always fall short of His glory and holiness. He is never not holy. His nature is holy, and His Name is holy. Our human nature keeps us from fully comprehending God's holiness.

On one family vacation, we trekked down into the depths of Carlsbad Caverns in New Mexico, behind a guide who looked too young to be responsible for a group of adults and children. The trails were well-lit, and handrails and guardrails helped us feel safe as we walked deeper and deeper into the caves. Once we were near the bottom, our guide told us about the absolute darkness we would be in if the lights on the path were turned off. Then he signaled for a colleague to pull the lever that extinguished them. The result was a blackness that made us gasp. It's an old saying, but it was true: "We couldn't see our hands in front of our faces." Complete darkness so black it was palpable. Finally, the guide struck a match, and I'll never forget the comfort and assurance and perspective that tiny flame provided. Darkness is not dark if there is even a spark of light.

You can bring a speck of light into darkness and it is no longer completely dark, but the opposite — bringing a speck of dark into the light — has no impact.

What does 1 John 1:5 say about God being light?

_____

God is more than a speck or flash of light because He is all light all the time. God is so holy, there is no trace of evil in His character. What traits in these verses show that God is uniquely holy?

Revelation 15:4 _____

Isaiah 59:16 _____

Revelation 4:8 _____

John 17:17 _____

Titus 1:2 _____

Knowing that God is holy and I am not holy knocks me to my knees and creates a lifestyle of repentance. You and I will never be perfect as long as we live in our fleshly bodies, but we can live a U-turn life as we walk the road of change. Paul wrote about our continual change in Romans 8:29:

"God knew what he was doing from the very beginning. He decided from the outset to shape the lives of those who love him along the same lines as the life of his Son. The Son stands first in the line of humanity he restored. We see the original and intended shape of our lives there in him" (The Message).

God's holiness and Jesus' humanity are the examples for us to follow as we try to imitate the Lord. Yet no holiness we conjure can match the holiness of God. Charles Spurgeon said, "Holiness is not the way to Christ; Christ is the way to holiness. Better still, Christ is our holiness." The word "holy" in the original language of both the Old and New Testament has the same root as "wholly," meaning complete.

Nineteenth century English scholar John Flavel, said, "What health is to the heart, holiness is to the soul."

Our First Place for Health strategy is to live a four-sided life, giving our all to the Lord — mind, heart, soul, and body. What is one practical step you can take to wholly commit yourself to God?

Mind _____
_____

Heart _____
_____

Soul _____
_____

Body _____
_____

When we consider the holiness of God, we could become discouraged and disheartened because we know we cannot attain His holiness. In 1 Peter 1:16 God calls us to be holy — " ... 'Be holy, because I am holy'" — but though He calls us to be perfect, He does not expect perfection from us. Psalm 103:14 reminds us why. Put the verse in your own words.

_____
_____

In Romans 8:38-39 Paul expresses how much God loves us, though we will never attain His perfect holiness. Of what does Paul say he is convinced?

_____

_____

_____

Lord, I desire to be holy, and I commit myself to You. Help me desire holiness even more. Never allow me to seek happiness over holiness.

—— DAY 5: DANIEL'S PRAYER

Lord, it seems easy to see sin in the world around me, but I admit it is not easy to recognize when sin has entered my heart. I am ready to repent.

Scripture tells the story of Daniel who, as a Jewish teenager, was taken captive into Babylon where he remained the rest of his life. Because he trusted God and stayed close to Him, Daniel's fame grew among each succeeding ruler. Even when Babylon was conquered and destroyed by the Medes, Daniel was distinguished as a wise man and interpreter of dreams.

Once a group of administrators that hated Daniel devised a plot against him. What does Daniel 6:4-5 say they learned?

_____

_____

_____

Since they couldn't find anything wrong with him, they formed a plan. According to Daniel 6:6-9, what did they do?

_____

_____

_____

When he heard about the new decree Daniel went home to an upstairs room and opened the windows toward Jerusalem; there, he prayed three times a day, giving thanks to God as he always had done.

As a great man of God who prayed three times a day, who set his heart on the purposes of God, Daniel had trusted Him in the lion's den many times before. We never once read about any sin or failure in Daniel's life or activities. We know he wasn't perfect — none of us is — but there are no records of any rebellion, disobedience, procrastination, or sins of any kind.

Knowing about Daniel's exemplary life makes his prayer in Chapter 9 even more remarkable. He had discerned from reading in Jeremiah that the desolation of Jerusalem would come to an end, and began to ask God to restore the great city. What did Daniel pray in verse 16?

_____

_____

_____

But before he asked God to restore Jerusalem, Daniel confessed (vs. 4). Read his confession in verses 4-19, and notice he says "we," "us," and "our" throughout the prayer (more than 30 times).

Do you find it remarkable that Daniel includes himself as he confesses Israel's sins? I do. It can be easy to pray for other people because we recognize their sins and failures, but it is more rare to see how we also have sinned. We don't have to look far to see sin in our nation — violence and looting, lying and deception, crime and dishonesty and injustice. America's young people seem to be turning from God. Jesus' precious Name is used as a curse. The pain and suffering of the oppressed are seen on the streets. Misinformation and lies are spread with the air of truth. How should we pray? Like Daniel, we must confess our sins along with the sins of the nation. Remember our rebellion, along with the rioting mobs' rebellion. Remember our lies, along with the false stories that flash across our screens. Remember our prejudices and failures, as we see groups that face bias and bigotry.

Confession sets the stage for a mighty work of God because confession leads to repentance. With confession and repentance, our relationship with God is restored and made stronger. Confession brings freedom.

What does David say in his prayer in Psalm 51:1-4 that causes you to see your need for confession and repentance?

_____

_____

_____

Oh Lord, we confess our sins. We know we have failed. Please heal our nation. We repent.

—— DAY 6: REFLECTION AND APPLICATION

Lord, I want to know You better. Show me some of Your characteristics.

God's Character A to Z

This week we've considered one of the most important characteristics of God — His holiness. Today, start the following exercise to get to know Him more — write a characteristic that begins with each letter (and breathe a breath of relief: I left out x, q, and z.).

A _____   M _____
B _____   N _____
C _____   O _____
D _____   P _____
E _____   R _____
F _____   S _____
G _____   T _____
H _____   U _____
I _____   V _____
J _____   W _____
K _____   Y _____
L _____

How does considering God's character A to Z affect your understanding of Romans 3:23?

_____
_____
_____

Lord, we are in awe of You. We praise Your wonderful Name.

—— DAY 7: REFLECTION AND APPLICATION

Lord, I want to revel in the glory of Who You are. Help me make time today for time with You.

Make Time for Him

Read the following Psalms. Then take a walk or sit alone outside in nature. Ask the Lord to reveal any part of your life or activities that don't match up to His best for you. Ask Him for the courage to repent, and for Him to open your eyes to the new path of His will.

Psalm 19
Psalm 57
Psalm 115

Now write an original psalm.

_____
_____
_____

Lord, You are majesty and glory. You reign over all nature and the universe. I praise Your Name.

WEEK EIGHT: STRENGTH WILL RISE BECAUSE ... I DON'T QUIT

SCRIPTURE MEMORY VERSE

The LORD himself goes before you and will be with you; he will never leave you nor forsake you. Do not be afraid; do not be discouraged. Deuteronomy 31:8

In her book, "Don't Quit/Get Fit," First Place for Health national director Vicki Heath writes:

> "When I started on my journey, I had so much to overcome. I had never been a disciplined person, and I realized early on that getting healthy and losing weight (were) going to cost me something. It was going to require some of the hardest work I had ever done. The same will be true for you. It will cost you some of your money, your time, your energy, and you will have to do without the foods you like to eat if they are not good for you. A life based on the principles of First Place for Health is a life of discipline and sacrifice — two words that are countercultural today."

Vicki's book describes four "fitness killers" that attack us and try to keep us from success in our wellness journey: no time, no motivation, no results, no stamina. These four victory-busters keep us weak in our quest for wellness, and they also can suck the life out of our spiritual journey.

The excuse of not having enough time is common because we fill each waking moment with activities for our kids, family, friends, job, church; and we leave little time for ourselves or God. Time constraints lead to frustration and can kill our motivation, and when we see few results, our energy and determination dwindle. It's a vicious cycle that can eventually lead to abandoning our dreams.

Paul encourages us to never give up:
"Let us not become weary in doing good, for at the proper time we will reap a harvest if we do not give up" (Galatians 6:9).
"I can do all this through him who gives me strength" (Philippians 4:13).

—— DAY 1: AI IS DESTROYED

Lord, I believe You call me to try again when I have failed. It seems much easier to quit and keep the status quo. I need Your strength to move forward.

At the end of Joshua 7, the Bible says the Lord turned from His fierce anger at Israel. At the beginning of Chapter 8, we see God stepping in and giving Joshua a command. What were the first words God said in Joshua 8:1?

_____

_____

_____

Why do you think God was encouraging the great leader? Consider Psalm 30:5, Matthew 11:28, and Isaiah 12:1 in your answer.

_____

_____

_____

When have you felt the hand of God's comfort in your life?

_____

_____

_____

Try Again

The Lord gave instructions to Joshua for a new attack on Ai. No matter our failures, the worst mistake is to not try again. Scottish preacher Alexander Whyte said the "victorious Christian life is a series of new beginnings."

If you feel you have failed and wonder why you should continue trying to find your path to a healthy lifestyle through First Place for Health, don't be discouraged about the past or fearful of the future. Be comforted by God's words in Joshua 8:1: "Do not be afraid; do not be discouraged."

God has a plan for you to begin again. According to 2 Chronicles 16:9, "The eyes of the LORD range throughout the earth to strengthen those whose hearts are fully committed to him."

Read Joshua 8:1-2 and list the main points of God's instruction to Joshua.

_____

_____

_____

Compare the instructions before the conquest of Jericho with those God gives in these verses. What is different about the plunder, loot, and livestock from the city?

_____

_____

_____

God never intended to deprive Israel of treasures from the cities they conquered. He gave the one-time command for Jericho, but for Ai He said to take it all. If only Achan had waited a few days, he would have been a wealthy man, and not put the nation in peril or lost his life and family. As Warren Wiersbe said, "God always gives his best to those who leave the choice with him."

The military strategy for Ai was the opposite for Jericho — the army marched together in daylight as God performed a mighty miracle at Jericho, but at Ai the army was separated into two flanks in a night operation, and won the battle militarily. God doesn't always give the same battle plan, nor does He drag out old strategies for us to try over and over. We must seek God's will for each new undertaking. We should hear God's voice in a fresh, new way each day.

I was once part of a Bible study at our church. Each week we discussed a passage, and much of it was rich and life-giving for me. But I noticed that some of the participants only spoke about how God had touched their lives or intervened in the past-tense. Way past — like 10 or 20 years ago. I longed to say, "Yes, but what encounter have you had with Him lately?"

The truth is, God has entered our lives more often and more dramatically than we deserve, but we might not see His hand if we are not alert. Maybe we see only the bad happening around us, or we are too busy, but God is always with us.

What does Romans 8:38-39 say about the closeness of God?

_____

_____

_____

List a difficult situation in the left column, and on the right, a way you have seen God's hand in a fresh way.

Difficult Situation   God's Fresh Touch

_____   _____
_____   _____
_____   _____
_____   _____
_____   _____

When I wake up each morning, I face several battles. Will I do the work that is waiting for me or will I find a way to procrastinate and play? Will I eat healthy food that nourishes my body, or will I choose fatty, salty foods with no nutritional value? Will I go for a walk and go to the gym, or will I sit in front of the TV? Will I spend time in the Word and seek God's face or will I rely on clichés and tired old sayings to feed my soul? God is fully present with us each day, in each situation and each moment. Even in the daily battles.

Jesus said, " ... I am with you always [remaining with your perpetually — regardless of circumstance, and on every occasion], even to the end of the age" (Matthew 28:20, AMP).

Theologian and writer A.W. Tozer noted, "An infinite God can give all of Himself to each of His children. He does not distribute Himself that each may have a part, but to each one He gives all of Himself as fully as if there were no others."
You have all of God's attention. He is with you for this moment; for this flash of joy or this tough season. Watch for Him and hear Him today.

We must not rely on old messages, techniques, or programs to reach a new generation. The message of Christ never changes, but methods do.

What positive changes have you noticed in your church? Your community? Your family?

_____
_____
_____

First Place is constantly improving the materials we use to help build healthy life-styles. What new product/book/resource has helped you?

_____

_____

_____

Lord, please give me a fresh touch and renewed courage to stick to it in First Place for Health and in my life as I follow You.

—— DAY 2: THE OFFERINGS

Lord, Israel made offerings to You throughout the year, which showed their commitment. Please help me become more focused on You and Your blessings each day.

Joshua interrupted military activity to lead Israel to make a new commitment to Jehovah. According to Joshua 8:30-31, what did he do?

_____

_____

The Israelites offered "burnt offerings and sacrificed fellowship offerings" on the altar Joshua built. The Old Testament revolves around a system of offerings, with five main sacrifices:

Burnt Offering
Grain Offering
Peace Offering
Purification Offering
Guilt Offering

These are meant to show God's grace; each is an outward expression of a desire to mend broken relationships with the Lord.

The Burnt Offering (first mentioned in Genesis 8:20; see also Leviticus 1)
Purpose: General atonement for sin and an expression of devotion to God
Type: Bull, sheep, goat, dove, or pigeon
Method: Burnt whole overnight
Fulfillment in Christ: He willingly gave His life for us

The most common sacrifice and, because the entire thing is burnt, indicates full surrender to the Lord.

How do Matthew 22:36-40 and Ephesians 5:2 show us the blessings of offering ourselves wholly to God?

_____

_____

_____

The Grain Offering (Leviticus 2)
Purpose: Freewill expression of devotion to God for His goodness and wisdom
Type: Cooked, unsweetened, and unleavened bread — baked, grilled, fried, roasted in oil; sometimes an additional "drink offering"
Method: Only a portion was burnt; the rest given to the priests for their meal
Fulfillment in Christ: He is the Bread of Life

This does not shed blood and is considered a "living sacrifice." Jesus was an obedient example.

What do Matthew 4:4 and Romans 12:1 tell us about becoming a living sacrifice in our walk with God?

_____

_____

_____

The Peace Offering (Leviticus 3)
Purpose: A meal between two or more parties before God in a spirit of fellowship and commitment to each other
Type: Cattle, sheep, or goat — male or female — always without blemish
Method: Some portion shared with priests, but to be eaten within two days and any leftovers to be burned
Fulfillment in Christ: He is our peace and our only reconciliation with God

Three Primary Types: Thanksgiving, Wave, Votive

This is the only sacrifice that allows the person offering it to eat a portion. It builds fellowship and communion.

What does 1 John 1:1-3 say about how the cross brings us into true fellowship with Jesus?

_____

_____

_____

The Purification Offering (also translated Sin Offering; Leviticus 4)
Purpose: Atonement for unintentional sin and to purify a person to enter the presence of God
Type: Unblemished animals, birds, or bread
Method: Personal — not to be shared
Fulfillment in Christ: He is our sin offering; He paid the price for our sin

We have all sinned and the penalty is death. This offering satisfied God's wrath for sin and made fellowship with Him possible.

How did Jesus offer the Sin Offering for us, once and for all (Galatians 2:20 and 2 Corinthians 5:21)?

_____

_____

_____

The Guilt Offering (sometimes called Trespass Offering; Leviticus 5)
Purpose: Repayment or compensation for a debt, especially due to a specific sin
Type: A specified monetary value
Method: The priest mitigated the debt and assessed a 20 percent fee.
Fulfillment in Christ: He died so every sin is forgiven and covered

First John 2:2 says this brings forgiveness of sin: "He is the atoning sacrifice for our sins, and not only for ours but also for the sins of the whole world."

According to 1 John 1:9, what must we do when we sin?

_____

Sacrifices provided a way for Israel to maintain their close relationship with Jehovah. Ultimately the system was inadequate, which is why Jesus came to offer the final sacrifice once and for all. The sacrifices give us a pattern for approaching God.

Read Hebrews 9:12 and 26. Explain how the offerings depict what Christ did for us and show His relationship with the Father.

_____

_____

_____

We don't quit, because Jesus gave His all for us.

Read 1 Samuel 15:22. What is better than sacrifice?

_____

Sacrifices for Health and Wellness
Sweat. When we exercise, we offer it to the Lord as a sacrifice of time, effort, and sweat to make our bodies strong enough to serve Him well.
Certain foods. When we recognize our trigger foods — those that get us off track, such as sweet or salty treats or fresh-baked bread — we can use that knowledge to eat foods that are nutritionally valuable and not junk to our bodies.
Rest. When we organize our busy schedules to include time for rest and renewal.
Peace. When we trust the Lord to work out all the details of a tough situation and allow Him to bring calm and order to our lives.
Stuff. When we purposefully limit our shopping, eating, and calendars to allow time to enjoy life and follow the leading of the Spirit.

Lord, I offer myself to You as a sacrifice that honors Your holiness and mercy. Please give me the courage to release areas of my life — selfish desires, cravings, ambitions for glory — for the greater good of following You.

—— DAY 3: JOSHUA: THE MAN, THE LEADER
Lord, I am fully committed to You. I give You my body — help me eat and exercise to become strong for You. I give You my mind — help me capture my thoughts. I give You my emotions — help me celebrate joy and hope, and not give in to anxiety and worry. I give You my spirit — help me be filled with Your Spirit in my thoughts and actions.

The Book of Joshua is all about beginnings — new land, new home, new identity, new faith, and a new leader. Joshua is the man who didn't quit.

The story of God's people focuses on Moses, whose life, ministry, teachings, and leadership impact Israel to this day. His successor was Joshua, who was born a slave. He lived through the oppression of Egypt and followed the great leader Moses across the Red Sea and into the Sinai desert. He watched his parents' generation murmur and complain against Moses — and God. He could have joined in the grumbling majority, but something was different about this young man.

Read Numbers 13:8 and 16. What was Joshua's given name and who was his father? What was the new name given to him by Moses?

_____

As the firstborn son of Nun, Hoshea was in danger the night of the last plague in Egypt, but his family trusted that the Lord would protect them on the night of Passover by the blood of the lamb on the doorpost. As a young man in Egypt, Hoshea would have witnessed the plagues and how God rescued the Israelites by opening the Red Sea.

Moses renamed him Joshua, which means, "Jehovah is salvation." Joshua grew into a man of faith. He also was a warrior — a general with exceptional military skill.

Read Exodus 17:8-16. Who attacked Israel? Describe the battle.

_____

_____

_____

The battle with Amalek was a test of Joshua's courage, faith, and leadership. When the Lord singled him out in verse 14, Joshua passed the assessment well. Many scholars believe Joshua's conflict with Amalek was preparation for the many battles he would fight in the Promised Land.

Read Exodus 24:13. What other role did Joshua take?

_____

The word "aide" also can be translated "servant" or "minister." Joshua served Moses and learned from this mighty mentor. After they came down from Mt. Sinai and discovered the Israelites had made a golden calf to worship, Joshua was with Moses in the Tent of Meeting as he judged the people.

Read Exodus 33:9-11. What did Moses do in that tent and who stayed when he left?

_____

_____

_____

This was a place of worship and communion with God. How do you think living there affected Joshua?

_____

_____

_____

Read Joshua 1:8 and 5:13-15. What is the secret of Joshua's skills and victories?

_____

_____

_____

As a slave, Joshua trusted God for redemption and freedom. How have you trusted God this week?

_____

_____

_____

As a warrior, Joshua's faith grew each time God brought a victory. What victory has grown your faith this week?

_____

_____

_____

As a servant (aide), Joshua gained skills in leadership and learned to worship God. Who has mentored you and what have you learned from him/her that has brought you closer to God?

_____

_____

_____

Read Deuteronomy 31:7, Joshua's "ordination service." What challenges did Moses give him?

_____

_____

_____

As a 20-year-old soldier, my husband boarded a plane to begin his trip to war-torn Vietnam. I stood on the tarmac (yes, then you could actually go out where the plane was loading) and watched him settle into his seat. We were terrified of the dangers that awaited him. He picked up his Bible, letting the pages fall open randomly. His eyes focused on this verse: "Be strong and courageous … do not be afraid" (Deuteronomy 31:7-8). This became our mantra for the next 14 months of separation and anxiety.

What circumstances are you facing right now that cause you to relate to these words to Joshua?

_____

_____

_____

Moses was a great leader and an example of faith and courage. He was a godly mentor to Joshua. Read Joshua 1:2-3 and describe his new circumstances.

_____

_____

_____

Lord, You have led me this far, giving me experiences and opportunities to grow my skills and grow closer to You. Whatever new circumstances You place me in, I know You will be with me as You were with Joshua.

—— DAY 4: THE VALLEY OF TROUBLE

Lord, I don't want to live in the valley of my troubles and pain, wallowing in my sin and rebellion. I know You can make a way.

When Joshua discovered the sin of Achan, who had stolen from the battlefield even though God had said "take nothing," Joshua brought the man and his family to justice at the Valley of Achor. This was the spot for Achan's trial, punishment, and eventual burial. Joshua 7:26c says, "Therefore that place has been called the Valley of Achor ever since."

The Hebrew word *achor* means trouble. More than misfortune, it is "severe afflic-tion," or a taboo of the place based on the disobedience of a man and his family. Condemnation and despair were heaped up in that valley like the stones that covered Achan and his possessions.

Achan thought, *I want the gold, silver, and robe so much*. His sin was greed. Name some of the consequences of his sin on Israel.

_____

_____

_____

We once had a family discussion about the various places my husband and I had lived, beginning with our first apartment. He was in the military, and we found a place near the gates of the army base. A large old house had been sectioned into seven tiny apartments, and we took one on the third floor. It was primitive, but fine. What we didn't realize was the name of that part of town — Snake Hill — well known for violence and crime. One snap decision in the daylight left 20-year-old me often there alone, with sirens and occasional screams in the night. My Valley of Trouble was called Snake Hill.

We thought of other decisions that had lifelong consequences. We once turned down a job in South Carolina that may have changed where we raised our children. We once changed churches because of a shorter commute. I took a job and put my kids in preschool — a temporary plan to get over a financial hump, which lasted more than 30 years. Some decisions became like a Valley of Trouble because of the effect on our lifestyle; some took us away from friends and into a time of loneliness.

What decisions have you made that became your Valley of Trouble? What event is associated with the deepest pain of your life?

_____

_____

_____

What decisions — or lack of — put you in the Valley of Trouble with your health or weight?

_____

_____

I've thought about this a lot, because I changed from a thin young woman into an overweight older woman without really understanding how it happened. Gradually I went from a size 6 to a size 12, then one day I realized I needed to buy extra-large; my shopping became about what would fit instead of what I liked. And suddenly I was in the Valley of Trouble because of my weight.

Whether your Valley of Trouble is food- or weight-related or financial- or relation-ship-related, it is not a nice place to be. Living there is difficult. Emotions run wild. Following God seems impossible. Relationships are shaky. We feel guilt, shame, re-morse, and regret. And like Achan, all we can say is, "Yes, I got myself into this mess because I saw it and I wanted it."

Read Isaiah 65:10. What does it say about the Valley of Achor?

_____

_____

What? We read these words and wonder how this pile of rocks could become a place to pasture flocks, and a resting place. Now read Hosea 2:15. What does it say about the valley?

_____

_____

God is able to transform our Valley of Trouble into a Door of Hope. Trouble is a result of sin, guilt, and even punishment, but our hope is our faith and the glorious forgive-ness of the Lord. "Hope" is a common word in the Bible, but in Joshua 2:18 and 24 the Hebrew word normally translated "hope" is "cord" — as in the scarlet cord Rahab let down to help the spies escape, and put in her window so the Israelites would rescue her. The cord is hope.

A door can be a gateway to freedom and reward. The familiar John 10:10 rings true: " ... I have come that they may have life, and have it to the full." And Jesus' words are true, even if we have made the worst mistakes or failed completely. He always opens a door of hope.

What does God do with our mourning? (Psalm 30:11-12)

_____

_____

_____

What does God do when we stumble? (Psalm 37:23-24)

_____

_____

_____

How does God handle our disasters? (Psalm 18:16-18)

_____

_____

_____

Sin will not ruin us, because God always rescues us and provides the opportunity to move forward again. Don't quit.

Lord, when we go through the worst of life — our Valley of Trouble — we are taken down to the pit. Thank You that You transform our troubled places into open gateways of hope, and that You never leave us.

—— DAY 5: THE RIVER
Lord, send your Holy Spirit to refresh my resolve and give me the audacity to never quit.

Sticking with our First Place for Health plan for exercise and eating nutritional food can be difficult. You and I have to wake up every morning with new energy and new resolve to keep from quitting.

At first it was easy because I was motivated by learning the plan and introducing colorful, delicious foods into my diet. I loved the feeling healthy food and exercise brought, and I loved watching the scale go down. Then life stepped in. A family gathering or big holiday, and the day-to-day effort to plan, cook, and track my food, or make the drive to the gym, went out the door. My early determination turned complacent and stale.

I remember a poem by John Greenleaf Whittier I learned in elementary school.

> "When things go wrong, as they sometimes will,
> When the road you're trudging seems all uphill,
> When the funds are low and the debts are high,
> And you want to smile, but you have to sigh,
> When care is pressing you down a bit,
> Rest, if you must, but don't you quit."

God has given His Holy Spirit to help us never quit. The Holy Spirit is like a river. Three of the Earth's most important bodies of water are river, lake, and ocean. Oceans are huge expanses of saltwater that cover about two-thirds of the Earth's surface. Lakes are surrounded by land; they do not empty into other waterways and typically are freshwater. A river is a free-flowing stream of fresh water that connects to a larger body of water.

While oceans go through tide cycles and are guided by the gravitational pull of the moon, lakes typically are stagnant and don't move unless there is wind.

Rivers, however, continually flow from the source to the sea; their waters move through your fingers when you put your hand in. How does this flowing compare to the role of the Holy Spirit? Ecclesiastes 1:7 and Isaiah 44:3 will help you answer.

_____

_____

_____

A river's waters flow from a single source, which seems never-ending. What is the source of the Holy Spirit's flow? Read Revelation 22:1 and John 7:38 to help you answer.

_____

_____

A river is life-giving to the plants, animals, and humans along its path. What does John 4:13-14 say about the water of the Holy Spirit?

_____

_____

Read Psalm 1:3 and describe the power of a river.

_____

_____

The Holy Spirit is our teacher. "But the Advocate, the Holy Spirit, whom the Father will send in my name, will teach you all things and will remind you of everything I have said to you" (John 14:26).

The Holy Spirit convicts us of sin. "When he comes, he will prove the world to be in the wrong about sin and righteousness and judgment" (John 16:8).

The Holy Spirit lives in us. "Don't you know that you yourselves are God's temple and that God's Spirit dwells in your midst?" (1 Corinthians 3:16).

The Holy Spirit guides us. "But when he, the Spirit of truth, comes, he will guide you into all the truth ... " (John 16:13).

Like a river flows, the Holy Spirit flows in and through us, and brings life-giving, refreshing water into our dry, parched lives.

Some may wonder how to receive the Holy Spirit, or when we receive Him. According to Acts 2:38, when does it take place?

_____

_____

When you give your heart to Jesus, the Holy Spirit takes residence there. Your job then is to allow Him to change you from the inside out. As you yield to Him, you will love others in a new way, and you will give grace to those who might otherwise make you angry or frustrated. The Holy Spirit produces "fruit" when He makes His home in our hearts.

Read Galatians 5:22 and beside the fruits of the Spirit, describe how each has changed your life.

Love _____

Joy _____

Peace _____

Forbearance (Patience) _____

Kindness _____

Goodness _____

Faithfulness _____

Gentleness _____

Self-Control _____

With the Holy Spirit flowing through us like a wonderful river, we will produce His fruit each day, and we will not quit in our journey to be stronger.

Lord, You fill me with wonderful love, joy, peace, patience, kindness, goodness, faithfulness, gentleness, and self-control. I'm so grateful You push me forward and never let me quit.

—— DAY 6: REFLECTION AND APPLICATION
Lord, remind me of the call You placed on my life.

This is Why We Don't Quit
Today is a good day to go back to the first verses in the Book of Joshua and remind ourselves why we need to find strength.

> "After the death of Moses, the LORD's servant, the LORD spoke to Joshua son of Nun, Moses' assistant. He said, 'Moses my servant is dead. Therefore, the time has come for you to lead these people, the Israelites, across the Jordan River into the land I am giving them'" (Joshua 1:1-2, NLT).

Notice God's instructions: "Therefore, the time has come for you to lead these people." These 11 words are Joshua's calling from God. Moses was dead. The wilderness years were over. Joshua was to take on a new role as leader of the people, and take them across the Jordan River into the Promised Land.

Joshua's call reminds me of another call found in Esther 4:14b when Mordecai says, "And who knows but that you have come to your royal position for such a time as this?"

Today, reflect on what God has called you to do. That calling is sacred and blessed. The Enemy would love to get you off course and strip your calling from you. But in those first verses of Joshua 1, we see how God will help us be true to our calling.

> God gave Joshua a promise: "I will give you every place where you set your foot ... " (Joshua 1:3).
> God promised power: "No one will be able to stand against you ... " (Joshua 1:5).
> God promised to never abandon Joshua: "I will never leave you nor forsake you" (Joshua 1:5).

God has called us and He equips us. These are the reasons we don't quit.

Lord, thank You for reminding me of my calling. I commit to follow Your lead as I do Your will. I know You will never quit me, and I promise to never quit You.

—— DAY 7: REFLECTION AND APPLICATION

Lord, I will continue to trust You. Even when quitting feels safer, I will take one more step with You.

Mountaineering or Mountain-nearing

David wrote, "LORD, who may dwell in your sacred tent? Who may live on your holy mountain?" (Psalm 15:1).

At the base of a mountain, a climber knows he/she must shed all unnecessary weight. We too must get rid of the weight of sin: " ... let us throw off everything that hinders and the sin that so easily entangles" (Hebrews 12:1b).

Maybe as you read these words you think: *Mountain-climbing? Me? Mountain-living maybe.*

> *Ah yes, the view from the top. Miles and miles of beauty before my eyes. Peacefully enjoying the panoramas and vistas. Snow in winter; wildflowers and critters in summer. Yes, mountaintop living is for me, but climbing — no thanks. From down here, the top of the mountain seems impossible. I feel lost in the valley of busyness and compromise; tangled in the weeds of bad habits, selfish attitudes, hurt feelings. I haven't had much time lately to gaze at the mountain, let alone plan a trip to the top. Besides, I tried climbing before and failed. Every step was slippery; dangerous precipices loomed; finding a handhold was tricky. Maybe mountain-climbing isn't for me. Yet something calls me — something says, "There's more to life than this valley, girl." More than everyday chores. More than shuffling papers and pushing computer keys. More than constant financial worries. More than the loneliness I sometimes feel in a crowd.*

Is God calling you to strength? Then let's climb. We may hit bumps and get bruised. We may need Band-Aids and liniment. But we're not climbing for the climb — we're not mountaineering. We are mountain-nearing — drawing close to the Lord each day. Commit to never quit climbing.

Lord, the Earth is Yours and everything in it. My heart longs to ascend the mountain of the Lord. I will continue in Your Word and claim Your gifts as I grow stronger each day.

WEEK NINE: STRENGTH WILL RISE BECAUSE ...
I CELEBRATE

The name of the LORD is a fortified tower; the righteous run to it and are safe.
Proverbs 18:10

What have you learned in this study that has made you stronger?

_____

_____

_____

_____

To help shape your (short) victory celebration testimony, work through the following in your prayer journal, one each day leading up to your group's celebration.

DAY ONE: List some of the benefits you have gained by allowing the Lord to transform your life through this nine-week First Place for Health session. Be mindful that He has been active in all four aspects of your being, so list benefits you have received in the physical, mental, emotional and spiritual realms.

DAY TWO: In what ways have you most significantly changed mentally? Have you seen a shift in the ways you think about yourself, food, your relationships, or God? How has Scripture memory been a part of these shifts?

DAY THREE: In what ways have you most significantly changed emotionally? Have you begun to identify how your feelings influence your relationship to food and exercise? What are you doing to stay aware of your emotions, both positive and negative?

DAY FOUR: In what ways have you most significantly changed spiritually? How has your relationship with God deepened? How has drawing closer to Him made a difference in the other three areas of your life?

DAY FIVE: In what ways have you most significantly changed physically? Have you met or exceeded your weight/measurement goals? How has your health improved during the past twelve weeks?

DAY SIX: Was there one person in your First Place for Health group who was particularly encouraging to you? How did their kindness make a difference in your First Place for Health journey?

DAY SEVEN: Summarize the previous six questions into a one-page testimony, or "faith story," to share at your group's victory celebration.

May our gracious Lord bless and keep you, and help you grow stronger because of your experiences, your encounters with Jesus, and your commitment to First Place for Health.

APPENDIX A

The Red Sea and Jordan River experiences are used as an analogy of what happens in our Christian life. The Apostle Paul also referenced them in 1 Corinthians 10. As with all analogies, the comparison will unravel if you carry it too far. But the basic theology of these religious-sounding words — justification, sanctification, and glorification — never unravels, especially if we understand the nature of the theology.

Justification is what happens at the moment of salvation. The colloquial terminology is, "just as if we had never sinned." Justification is a nuanced word that basically means we are judged not guilty for our sins because Jesus paid our penalty.

Sanctification is a process, not a moment. It is continuous and progressive; what God does through and to us to make us more like Jesus. We never totally arrive at sanctification until we get to Heaven. But throughout life's journey, we grow closer to God as we learn to obey Him fully and commit every aspect of our lives to Him.

Just as Israel had Moabites and Goliaths and battles in the Promised Land, we will face spiritual battles, giants, and trials. As we trust the Lord and grow spiritually toward righteousness, we will get a glimpse of that abundant life Jesus spoke of in John 10:10.

We are set free from sin through salvation (justification) and now we become slaves to righteousness (Romans 6:18). As we move through our Christian life, we move toward sanctification as we push our lusts and worldly desires away. With the help of the Holy Spirit, we do not allow sin to control us (Ephesians 1:13-14).

Glorification happens when we enter Heaven and are given new existence in His presence. In her classic work, "The Christian's Secret of a Happy Life," written in 1875, Hannah Whitall Smith describes justification, sanctification, and glorification this way: "I have been saved. I am being saved. I will be saved."[1]

---

[1] Adapted from "The Christian's Secret of a Happy Life" by Hannah Whitall Smith

APPENDIX B

As a bonus memory project, read and memorize Psalm 114:1-7, which summarizes in beautiful poetry what happened when the nation of Israel came out of Egypt.

"When Israel came out of Egypt,
 Jacob from a people of foreign tongue,
Judah became God's sanctuary,
 Israel His dominion.
The sea looked and fled,
 the Jordan turned back;
the mountains leaped like rams,
 the hills like lambs.
Why was it, sea, that you fled?
  Why, Jordan, did you turn back?
Why, mountains, did you leap like rams,
 you hills, like lambs?
Tremble, Earth, at the presence of the Lord,
 at the presence of the God of Jacob ... "

LEADER DISCUSSION GUIDE

For in-depth information, guidance and helpful tips about leading a successful First Place for Health group, spend time studying the *My Place for Leadership* book. In it, you will find valuable answers to most of your questions, as well as personal insights from many First Place for Health group leaders.

For the group meetings in this session, be sure to read and consider each week's discussion topics several days before the meeting—some questions and activities require supplies and/or planning to complete. Also, if you are leading a large group, plan to break into smaller groups for discussion and then come together as a large group to share your answers and responses. Make sure to appoint a capable leader for each small group so that discussions stay focused and on track (and be sure each group records their answers!).

—— WEEK ONE: STRENGTH WILL RISE BECAUSE ... I DECIDE

One goal for this week is to get to know class members spiritually. Discussion about the Red Sea will help each one identify that moment when they decided personally to accept Christ as Lord and Savior. As the leader, be prepared to present the salvation plan to the class. There are a number of ways to explain how God sent His Son to pay the price for our sins and rescue us from the slavery and bondage of sin. Perhaps the simplest is Acts 16:30-31, when a jailer asked the question of his prisoners, Paul and Silas: "Sirs, what must I do to be saved?" They replied, "Believe in the Lord Jesus, and you will be saved — you and your household."

Another clear way to explain salvation is the "Roman Road."

First: Acknowledge God as creator and sustainer of life: "You are worthy, our Lord and God, to receive glory and honor and power, for you created all things, and by your will they were created and have their being" (Revelation 4:11).

Second: Recognize that we are all sinners: " ... for all have sinned and fall short of the glory of God." (Romans 3:23).

Third: Understand that the penalty for sin is death: "For the wages of sin is death, but the gift of God is eternal life in Christ Jesus our Lord" (Romans 6:23).

Fourth: Know that God loved us so much, He provided a way to rescue us: "But God demonstrates his own love for us in this: While we were still sinners, Christ died for us" (Romans 5:8).

The second goal for the week is to help your class understand the abundant life Jesus offers every believer. (Check Appendix A for a brief discussion of the theology of justification, sanctification, and glorification.) During the meeting, ask some of the following:

1) What do you think is a good "abundant life" mentality, and how do we begin to take steps to live to the full, as Jesus said in John 10:10? Use Day Three's lesson to talk about making decisions.

2) What part does gratitude play in living the abundant life?

3) What habits, such as starting the day with prayer and Bible reading, will help us live each day to the full? Get as many varied suggestions as possible, including spiritual time with God, exercise, healthy foods, positive conversations, helping others, etc. Draw attention to the study on Day Four about taking action.

4) How does knowing your strengths and challenges help you live a fuller life? Here is an opportunity to talk about the importance of the My Discovery books and the personality tests there.

5) What practical steps can we take to develop a deeper spiritual life and follow Jesus more closely? Focus on the last two questions of Day Five to help members see how FP4H helps us live healthier, but also make big changes in our spiritual journey.

Review the memory verse and discuss what the "holy life" means to each believer.

—— WEEK TWO: STRENGTH WILL RISE BECAUSE … I SUFFER

From Day One, discuss the idea of being used as a weapon in God's hands. Ask how this concept changes our perspective during troubles and trials.

Discuss the quote from Day Two by Nicolas Wolterstorff, asking members to explain the depth of God sharing our suffering.

On Day Three we discussed ways to become stronger in the four areas of life — physical, mental, emotional, and spiritual. Discuss these answers with the group and take note of fresh, new, practical ways they identify.

Ask if anyone has seen how God protected them from a much worse situation even though they had to go through a difficult place. Also discuss how going through a wilderness helped them cope with difficulty. Read Galatians 3:11 in The Message (quoted in Day Three) and discuss the various definitions of embrace (grasp, clutch, grab, hang on, enfold, snuggle, entwine).

Ask each member to identify what kind of marker they decided to build as a result of Day Five's lesson. Why was this important enough to remember with a memorial?

According to our memory verse this week, God is our strength. Ask class members to describe what knowing "God is strong" means to them right now.

—— WEEK THREE: STRENGTH WILL RISE BECAUSE ... I MAKE A VOW

God's Word can seem confusing because the principles He asks us to live by may feel upside-down to our logical minds. Our memory verse this week tells us to save our life by losing it, and we consider what it means to die to self as we look at taking a vow.

On Day One we considered what it means to become an apprenticed disciple. Ask your class to discuss practical steps they found for how we, as disciples, can become duplicators of Jesus' actions.

We were prompted on Day Two to give a definition of covenant. Ask the class to share their definitions. What does the lesson say about who gave the rite of circumcision and what it ultimately was intended to show?

Day Three brought us to discover that Jesus gives us a new identity. Ask class members to describe how a wandering mentality can harm our FP4H journey. We also learned we must *take off* the old and *put on* the new. Ask members to describe how they have changed their "wardrobe."

We saw an unusual phrase on Day Five about the land of the Hittites. Ask members to describe their personal land of the Hittites (secret no-man's land) and how God has helped them conquer this part of their lives.

During Days Six and Seven, we looked at the problem of time management, and how we can stay too busy and not make time for our souls. Ask your class to describe what steps they will take to reclaim some of their time.

—— WEEK FOUR: STRENGTH WILL RISE BECAUSE ... I WAIT

This week we delved into the difficulty of waiting and being uncertain of the future, and trusting God instead of being impatient.

On Day One we studied the idea of resting while we wait. What did Hebrews 4:1 say about the status of true rest? As we dissected Philippians 4:6-8, what discovery did class members make about how they can learn to rest and have peace?

On Day Two we noticed how Joshua worked while he waited. God expects us to do all we can. How does working while you wait exhibit faith? What did each member decide to do while they wait on God?

Day Three focused on healing while we wait. Ask the class to discuss additional ideas for practical steps toward healing.

Getting to know Jesus while you wait was the topic of Day Four. Joshua personally met Jesus in a face-to-face encounter. How did He encourage him? How does knowing Jesus encourage you?

Day Five urged us to celebration for what the Lord has done. Ask members to describe what Communion (the Lord's Supper) means to them.

Days Six and Seven challenged us to wait well. How can we be filled with power while we wait?

—— WEEK FIVE: STRENGTH WILL RISE BECAUSE … I OBEY

The Matthew 7:24 memory verse reminds us to hear God's words, but also put them into practice. The rest of the chapter describes two men — one who built his house on sand and one who built his house on rock. How can that story help us as we learn to obey God?

We discovered on Day One that the manna of the wilderness stopped on the day after Passover, when the people began to eat from the produce of the land. What did you learn about eating produce contrasted with eating manna that fell like rain? Ask class members to consider the difference between wilderness thinking and Promised Land thinking when it comes to food.

Day Two introduced the term "the fasted life." Ask the class what they learned about this way of life and how they will change their eating — and other — habits because of it.

Obedience was the topic of Day Three. We learned from the Beatitudes in Matthew 5 about our attitudes. What brought a new perspective about obedience?

On Day Four we saw Rahab's extraordinary faith and obedience. What did she know about God and how did that knowledge grow her faith?

On Day Five we saw the incredible blessings of living with faith and obedience. Our lives are more balanced, and we begin to focus on others instead of ourselves.

What did members learn on Days Six and Seven about the grandeur and power of God?

—— WEEK SIX: STRENGTH WILL RISE BECAUSE ... I FOLLOW

God rescued Israel from Egypt and assured abundant life in the Promised Land. Yet even though they detoured in the wilderness for 40 years, God's plan never changed.

We acknowledged on Day One that we can build walls around ourselves similar to those of Jericho. Discuss the kinds of walls we have built.

Make sure the class saw on Day Two how the instructions of God to Joshua were more detailed than those Joshua gave the people. Remind them that the Israelites didn't know the plan was to march for seven days. How does the term "keep walking" make a difference in your FP4H journey?

On Day Three we compared walls to strongholds we allow to be built; but with God's help, we can tear them down. Our real battle comes when we try to rebuild those walls. What does 1 Corinthians 15:57 say about victory? Ask members to describe any food strongholds they have battled.

We discovered on Day Four that God orders our steps and has an "on purpose" for each of us. Help your class see how God intends good for each person, and how each one can serve God in a unique way. Ask them to share a big item from their spiritual bucket list.

Day Five encouraged us to take our eyes off ourselves and follow God even if it doesn't make sense, and Day Six showed us how victory is possible.

Ask class members to explain the three statements from Day Seven.

—— WEEK SEVEN: STRENGTH WILL RISE BECAUSE ... I REPENT

God asks us to return to Him when we have strayed. Dick Eastman, international president of Every Home for Christ, says, "Confession is what you do on the way down to your knees, and repentance is what you do on the way back up." How does this describe what you have learned about repentance this week?

Day One names one of the most difficult sins to overcome: pride. How does pride play a part in your First Place for Health wellness quest?

We learned on Day Two how even our defeats can become a place of learning and growing. What does Hebrews 6:1 say about going back?

We discovered on Day Three that no sin should rule in our life, so we must repent. Discuss the differences between guilt, remorse, regret, and repentance.

On Day Four we zeroed in on the reason we must repent — the holiness of God. What unique traits did you discover about God?

Even Daniel repented. He was blameless and honorable and we never read about any sin — yet he includes himself in his prayer of confession. What did you learn about repentance on Day Five?

Days Six and Seven presented some of the amazing, glorious characteristics of our God. Which ones did you name?

—— WEEK EIGHT: STRENGTH WILL RISE BECAUSE … I DON'T QUIT

Quitting is such a human failing. We would love to walk away from anything that is hurtful or annoying. But quitting can sometimes cause us to abandon our dreams. In Galatians 6:9 Paul encouraged us to never give up: "Let us not become weary in doing good … ."

We saw on Day One how God defeated Ai using military tactics even after the army had failed in the first battle. Discuss the statement, "No matter our failures, the worst mistake is to not try again."

On Day Two we researched the various offerings Israel presented. They were a way for the people to maintain their close relationship with God. How was Jesus the ultimate offering that put an end to these various sacrifices?

We took a deeper look on Day Three at the man named Joshua. What did you learn about him? How does the record of his faith encourage you?

On Day Four the Valley of Trouble got a new name. What is that name, according to Hosea 2:15? How does knowing it encourage you when you face trouble?

We found a resource on Day Five for our health journey — the Holy Spirit. How is the Holy Spirit like a river? How does He help us?

On Days Six and Seven we discovered that our calling is why we don't quit, and we took a new look at finding God's "holy hill" in our Christian life and in our wellness. What encouragement did you receive that will help you never quit?

—— WEEK NINE: STRENGTH WILL RISE BECAUSE … I CELEBRATE

As your class members reflect on each week's content, help them remember the ways strength has risen because of following Christ fully in each area of life. Ask: What have you learned in this study that has made you stronger?

FIRST PLACE FOR HEALTH
JUMP START MENUS

All recipe and menu nutritional information was determined using the Master-Cook software, a program that accesses a database containing more than 6,000 food items prepared using the United States Department of Agriculture (USDA) publications and information from food manufacturers. As with any nutritional program, MasterCook calculates the nutritional values of the recipes based on ingredients. Nutrition may vary due to how the food is prepared, where the food comes from, soil content, season, ripeness, processing and method of preparation. For these reasons, please use the recipes and menu plans as approximate guides. As always, consult your physician and/or a registered dietitian before starting a weight-loss program.

For those who need more calories,

add the following to the 1,400–1,500 calorie plan:

1,500-1,600 calories:	1 oz.-eq of protein, 1 oz.-eq. grains, ½ cup vegetables, 1 tsp. healthy oils
1,700-1,800 calories:	1½ oz.-eq. of protein, 2 oz.-eq. grains, 1 cup of vegetables, 1 tsp. healthy oils
1,900-2,000 calories:	2 oz.-eq. of protein, 2 oz.-eq. of grains, 1 cup vegetables, ½ cup fruit, 1 tsp. healthy oils
2,100-2,200 calories:	3 oz.-eq. of protein, 3 oz.-eq. grains, 1½ cup vegetables, ½ cup fruit, 2 tsp. healthy oils
2,300-2,400 calories:	4 oz.-eq. of protein, 4 oz.-eq. of grains, 2 cups vegetables 3 cups frit, 3 tsp. healthy oils

Greek Omelet Muffins

Cooking spray
2 tablespoons extra-virgin olive oil
¾ cup diced onion
¼ teaspoon salt, divided
1 medium red bell pepper, diced
1 tablespoon finely chopped fresh oregano
8 large eggs
¾ cup crumbled feta cheese
½ cup low-fat milk
½ teaspoon ground pepper
2 cups chopped fresh spinach
¼ cup sliced Kalamata olives

Preheat oven to 325 degrees F. Liberally coat a 12-cup muffin tin with cooking spray.

Heat oil in a large skillet over medium heat. Add onion and 1/8 teaspoon salt; cook, stirring, until starting to soften, about 3 minutes. Add bell pepper and oregano; cook, stirring, until the vegetables are tender and starting to brown, 4 to 5 minutes. Remove from heat and let cool for 5 minutes.

Whisk eggs, feta, milk, pepper and the remaining 1/8 teaspoon salt in a large bowl. Stir in spinach, olives and the vegetable mixture. (Can make ahead up to this point. Refrigerate overnight and bake the next morning.)

Divide among the prepared muffin cups. Bake until firm to the touch, about 25 minutes. Let stand for 5 minutes before removing from the tin. Serves 6

Nutritional Information for 2 Omelets: 226 calories; protein 12.7g; carbohydrates 6.7g; fiber 1.3g; fat 16.7g; cholesterol 265.7mg; sodium 465.7mg

Hearty Tomato Soup with Beans & Greens

2 (14 ounce) cans hearty-style tomato soup
1 tablespoon olive oil
3 cups chopped kale
1 teaspoon minced garlic
1/8 teaspoon crushed red pepper (optional)
1 (14 ounce) can no-salt-added cannellini beans, rinsed
1/4 cup grated Parmesan cheese

Heat soup in a medium saucepan according to package directions; simmer over low heat as you prepare kale. Heat oil in a large skillet over medium heat. Add kale and cook, stirring, until wilted, 1 to 2 minutes. Stir in garlic and crushed red pepper (if using) and cook for 30 seconds. Stir the greens and beans into the soup and simmer until the beans are heated through, 2 to 3 minutes. Divide the soup among 4 bowls. Serve topped with Parmesan. Serves 4

Nutritional Information (1 1/4 cups): 200 calories; 5.8 g total fat; 4 mg cholesterol; 355 mg sodium; 29 g carbohydrates; 5.9 g fiber; 8.6 g protein;

Garlic Butter Chicken with Lemon Asparagus

3 boneless, skinless chicken breasts, cut into bite-sized chunks

2 bunch of asparagus, rinsed and trimmed

1/2 cup butter, softened

1 teaspoon olive oil

2 teaspoons minced garlic

1 teaspoon Italian seasoning

1 tablespoon hot sauce, optional

1/2 cup low-sodium chicken broth

Juice of 1/2 lemon

1 tablespoon minced parsley

Crushed red chili pepper flakes, optional

Slices of lemon, for garnish

For the chicken seasoning:

1 teaspoon salt

1 teaspoon fresh cracked black pepper

2 teaspoons onion powder

Slice chicken breasts into bite-sized chunks and season with salt, pepper, and onion powder. Let sit in a shallow plate while you prepare the asparagus. Wash and trim the ends of the asparagus, then blanch them in boiling water for 2 minutes, then soak in ice water to stop the cooking. This way, asparagus will cook faster and evenly in the skillet. You can skip this step if you have skinny asparagus. Drain and set aside. Heat half butter and olive oil in a large cast-iron skillet over medium-low heat. Gently stir-fry the chicken bites on all sides until golden brown. Lower the temperature, add one teaspoon minced garlic and Italian seasoning and stir and cook with chicken bites until fragrant. Remove the chicken bites from the skillet and set aside to a plate. You might have to work in batches to avoid crowding the pan and have steamed chicken bites instead of brown. In the same skillet over medium-high, add minced garlic then de-glaze with chicken broth. Bring to a simmer and allow to reduce to half the volume. Add remaining butter, lemon juice, hot sauce, parsley. Give a quick stir to combine. Add the blanched asparagus and toss for 2 minutes to cook it up. Add the sautéed chicken bites back to the pan and stir for another minute to reheat. Garnish the chicken and asparagus with more parsley, crushed chili pepper, and lemon slices and serve your garlic butter chicken bites and asparagus immediately. Serves 4

Nutritional Information: 515 calories; 14.8 g total fat; 62.3 g carbohydrates; 63 mg cholesterol; 747 mg sodium; 33.9 g protein

DAY 2 | BREAKFAST

Bacon & Broccoli Burrito

1 slice bacon
1 cup chopped broccoli
¼ cup chopped tomato
1 large egg
1 tablespoon reduced-fat milk
1 scallion, sliced
⅛ teaspoon salt
⅛ teaspoon ground pepper
1 teaspoon canola or avocado oil
2 tablespoons shredded sharp Cheddar cheese

Cook bacon in a medium nonstick skillet over medium heat, turning once or twice, until crisp, 4 to 6 minutes. Remove to a paper towel-lined plate. Add broccoli to the pan and cook, stirring, until soft, about 3 minutes. Stir in tomato and transfer to a small bowl.

Meanwhile, whisk egg, milk, scallion, salt and pepper in another bowl. When the vegetables are cooked, remove from skillet. Add oil and heat over medium heat. Add the egg mixture, tilting to coat the bottom of the pan. Cook without stirring until set, about 2 minutes. Using a spatula, carefully flip the egg. Sprinkle with cheese and cook until completely set, about 1 minute more. Transfer to a plate. Fill the lower half of the egg tortilla with the broccoli mixture and top with the bacon. Carefully roll into a burrito. Serves 1

Nutritional Information: 259 calories; protein 15.4g; carbohydrates 9.8g; fiber 3.3g; fat 18.2g; cholesterol 210mg; sodium 632.3mg

Greek Salmon Bowl

1 pound salmon fillet
1/2 teaspoon salt, divided
1/4 teaspoon ground pepper
8 ounces string beans, trimmed and cut into 1-inch pieces
1 3/4 cups water
3/4 cup quinoa, rinsed
3 tablespoons lemon juice
2 tablespoons olive oil
1 clove garlic, minced
2 teaspoons chopped fresh oregano or 1/2 tsp. dried
1 medium tomato, seeded and chopped
1/4 cup crumbled feta cheese
1/4 cup pitted Kalamata olives, halved or sliced

Preheat oven to 400 degrees. Line a large baking sheet with foil. Place salmon on the prepared baking sheet and sprinkle with salt and pepper. Bake until the salmon is no longer opaque in the center and flakes easily with a fork, 20 to 25 minutes. Let rest for 5 minutes, then flake the salmon into bite-size pieces (discard the skin). Meanwhile, bring 1 inch of water to a boil in a medium saucepan fitted with a steamer basket. Add beans; cover and cook until tender-crisp, about 5 minutes. Rinse the beans under cold water, drain well, and set aside. Combine water, quinoa, and 1/8 tsp. salt in the saucepan; bring to a boil. Reduce heat to low, cover, and simmer until the quinoa is tender and most of the liquid has been absorbed, 15 to 20 minutes. Fluff with a fork. Whisk lemon juice, oil, garlic, oregano, and the remaining 1/4 tsp. salt in a small bowl. To serve, divide the quinoa among 4 dinner bowls. Arrange the salmon, beans, tomato, feta, and olives over the quinoa. Drizzle with the dressing and garnish with more fresh oregano, if desired. Serves 4

Nutritional Information: 484 calories; 28 g total fat; 69 mg cholesterol; 577 mg sodium; 28 g carbohydrates; 30 g protein

Live It Tracker: 4 oz-eq. Protein, 1 oz-eq. Grain, 1/2 cup Vegetables, 1/2 tsp Healthy Oil

Lemon-Garlic Chicken Penne with Pesto

1 tablespoon finely grated lemon peel

1/4 cup lemon juice

2 tablespoons minced garlic

11/4 pounds bone-in chicken breast halves, skinned

1/4 teaspoon ground black pepper

1/8 teaspoon salt

11/4 cups whole wheat penne pasta

1/4 cup dried tomatoes (not oil-packed)

1/4 cup pesto

1 tablespoon minced garlic

1/4 cup reduced-sodium chicken broth

1 (9 ounce) package baby spinach

1/4 teaspoon crushed red pepper

1/8 teaspoon salt

4 teaspoons grated Parmesan cheese

For marinade, in a small bowl, combine lemon peel, lemon juice and 2 tablespoons garlic. Place chicken in a resealable plastic bag. Pour marinade over chicken. Seal bag and turn to coat chicken. Marinate in refrigerator for 30 minutes, turning bag occasionally. Preheat oven to 375 degrees. Drain chicken and discard marinade. Sprinkle chicken with black pepper and 1/8 teaspoon salt. Place chicken in a foil-lined shallow roasting pan. Roast for 40 minutes or until an instant-read thermometer inserted into inside thigh muscle registers 165 degrees. Allow to cool before removing meat from the bone and shred or cut into bite-size pieces. Cook pasta according to package directions; drain. Meanwhile, place dried tomatoes in a small bowl; pour enough hot water over tomatoes to cover and let stand until tomatoes are softened. Cut softened tomatoes into thin bite-size strips. In a large skillet, heat broth over medium heat until boiling. Add spinach; cook and stir about 1 minute or until spinach starts to wilt. Add chicken, crushed red pepper and 1/8 teaspoon salt. Cook about 2 minutes more or until spinach is completely wilted. Stir in cooked pasta, pesto, and dried tomatoes. Cook about 5 minutes or until chicken is heated through (165 degrees F). Sprinkle with 4 teaspoons Parmesan cheese. Serves 4

Nutritional Information: 348 calories; 11.4 g total fat; 76 mg cholesterol; 433 mg sodium; 26.7 g carbohydrates; 2.8 g fiber; 34.8 g protein

Veggie Scramble

2 teaspoons olive oil
1 cup chopped broccoli, asparagus and/or zucchini
1 small clove garlic, minced
½ teaspoon minced fresh rosemary
2 large eggs
1 tablespoon heavy cream
⅛ teaspoon salt
¼ teaspoon ground pepper
1 tablespoon shredded Cheddar cheese

Heat oil in an 8-inch skillet over medium-low heat. Add chopped vegetables. Cook, stirring often, until just about tender, 2 to 4 minutes. Stir in garlic and rosemary; cook for 1 minute more.

Crack eggs into a small bowl and whisk in cream, salt and pepper. Pour the egg mixture over the cooked vegetables. Stir until eggs are almost set. Add cheese; turn off the heat and let the eggs melt the cheese. Serves 1

Nutritional Information: 338 calories; protein 16.6g; carbohydrates 7.9g; fiber 2.6g; fat 27g; cholesterol sodium 512.8mg

Grilled Eggplant Sandwich

1 small clove garlic, chopped
1/4 cup low-fat mayonnaise
1 teaspoon lemon juice
1 medium eggplant, sliced into 1/2-inch rounds
2 large Portobello mushroom caps, gills removed
Canola or olive oil cooking spray
1/2 teaspoon salt
1/2 teaspoon freshly ground pepper
8 slices whole-wheat sandwich bread, lightly grilled or toasted
2 cups arugula, or spinach, stemmed and chopped if large
1 large tomato, sliced

Preheat grill to medium-high. Mash garlic into a paste on a cutting board with the back of a spoon. Combine with mayonnaise and lemon juice in a small bowl. Set aside. Coat both sides of eggplant rounds and mushroom caps with cooking spray and season with salt and pepper. Grill the vegetables, turning once, until tender and browned on both sides: 2 to 3 minutes per side for eggplant, 3 to 4 minutes for mushrooms. Slice the mushrooms. Spread 1 1/2 teaspoons of the garlic mayonnaise on each piece of bread. Layer the eggplant, mushrooms, arugula (or spinach) and tomato slices onto 4 slices of bread and top with the remaining bread. Serves 4

Nutritional Information: 289 calories; 10.5 g total fat; 4 mg cholesterol; 681 mg sodium; 40.3 g carbohydrates; 7.9 g fiber; 10.1 g protein

Honey-Garlic Chicken Thighs with Carrots & Broccoli

1/3 cup honey
11/2 tablespoons reduced sodium soy sauce
1 1/2 tablespoons minced garlic
1 tablespoon cider vinegar
1/4 teaspoon crushed red pepper
8 (5 ounce) bone-in, skin-on chicken thighs
1 pound small carrots, sliced into 1/2-inch pieces
2 tablespoons olive oil, divided
4 cups broccoli florets
1/2 teaspoon salt
1/2 teaspoon ground pepper
1 teaspoon cornstarch

Whisk honey, soy sauce, garlic, vinegar and crushed red pepper in a small bowl. Place chicken and half of the honey mixture (about 1/4 cup) in a zip-top plastic bag; remove excess air and seal bag. Massage the chicken in the sealed bag until well coated. Refrigerate for at least 30 minutes and up to 2 hours. Reserve the remaining honey mixture. Preheat oven to 400 degrees. Line a large rimmed baking sheet with foil; coat with cooking spray. Remove the chicken from the marinade (discard marinade); arrange on 1 side of the prepared pan. Combine carrots and 1 tablespoon oil in a medium bowl; toss well to coat. Spread the carrots in an even layer on the other side of the pan. Bake the chicken and carrots for 15 minutes. Remove from the oven; stir the carrots. Combine broccoli and the remaining 1 tablespoon oil; toss well to coat. Distribute the broccoli evenly over the chicken and carrots on the pan. Sprinkle salt and pepper over all. Bake until the vegetables are tender and a thermometer inserted in the thickest portion of the chicken registers 165 degrees F, 15 to 18 minutes. Meanwhile, whisk cornstarch and water in a small bowl until no clumps remain. Combine the cornstarch mixture and the reserved honey mixture in a small saucepan; bring to a simmer over medium-low heat, whisking once or twice. Simmer, whisking often, until the sauce is clear and thickened, about 2 minutes. Drizzle over the chicken and vegetables. Serve hot. Serves 4

Nutritional Information: 475 calories; 20.1 g total fat; 115 mg cholesterol; 686 mg sodium; 39.7 g carbohydrates; 5.1 g fiber; 35.8 g protein

DAY 4 | BREAKFAST

Pumpkin Smoothie

1/2 medium frozen banana
1/2 cup almond milk (can use low-fat milk)
1/2 cup whole milk Greek yogurt
1/2 cup canned pumpkin puree
1-2 teaspoon maple syrup

Place banana, almond milk (or other nut milk), yogurt, pumpkin puree, pumpkin pie spice and maple syrup in a blender. Blend until smooth. Serves 1

Nutritional Information: 247 calories; protein 10.2g; carbohydrates 41.9g; fiber 5.9g; fat 6.1g; cholesterol 10.9mg; sodium 120.5mg

Rotisserie Chicken Burritos

2 teaspoons extra-virgin olive oil

1/2 cup chopped red onion

1 teaspoon minced garlic

1 (15 ounce) can black beans, rinsed

1/2 cup water

1 tablespoon minced chipotle pepper in adobo sauce

2 cups shredded cooked chicken

2 cups chopped kale

1 cup reduced-fat sharp Cheddar cheese

2 tablespoons chopped fresh cilantro

½ teaspoon grated lime zest (optional)

1 tablespoon fresh lime juice

¼ teaspoon salt

4 (8 inch) whole-wheat tortillas

Heat oil in a large nonstick skillet over medium heat. Add onion and garlic; cook, stirring often, until the onion starts to soften, about 2 minutes. Add beans, water and chipotle; bring to a simmer, mashing slightly with the back of a spatula. Stir in chicken and kale; cook until thickened, 1 to 2 minutes. Remove from heat. Stir in Cheddar, cilantro, lime zest, lime juice and salt. Spread 3/4 cup filling on the bottom third of each tortilla, then roll tightly, burrito-style. Serves 4

Make-ahead Tip: Individually wrap the burritos tightly in foil and place in a seal-able plastic bag. Freeze for up to 3 months. To reheat one frozen burrito, unwrap and transfer to a microwave-safe plate. Cover with a paper towel and microwave on High until heated through, 2 to 3 minutes. Serves 4

Nutritional Information: 375 calories; 8.7 g total fat; 30 mg cholesterol; 854 mg sodium; 44.3 g carbohydrates; 0.7 g fiber; 26.5 g protein

One Pan Zucchini Chicken Enchiladas

2 Tbsp. olive oil
1 medium onion, chopped
2 cloves garlic, minced
1/2 cup frozen corn
1/2 black beans, drained and rinsed
2 tsp. chili powder
2 tsp. ground cumin
3 cups shredded cooked chicken
1/2 cup tomato salsa
1 cup red enchilada sauce, divided
1 cup shredded Mexican blend cheese, divided
2 lbs. zucchini, about 3 medium
Kosher salt and fresh black pepper

Heat oil in a large skillet over medium heat. Add onions and garlic, and cook 3-4 minutes, or until soft. Stir in corn, beans, chili powder, and cumin. Then add the shredded chicken. Remove skillet from heat and stir in salsa, 1/4 cup enchilada sauce, and 1/2 cup cheese. Season the mixture with salt and pepper, to taste. Preheat the oven to 375 degrees F. Line a sheet pan (casserole dish not recommended) with parchment paper and set aside. If using aluminum foil, lightly spray with a non-stick spray. Trim the ends of the zucchini and using a vegetable peeler, peel zucchini into thin ribbons. First few are usually too skinny to use. You can also use a mandolin slicer. You need a total of 42 zucchini ribbons. On a cutting board, lay out 3 ribbons of zucchini slightly overlapping each other. Add generous 1/4 cup of chicken mixture and tightly roll up the zucchini. Transfer to the sheet pan seam down, creating two rows of seven in the middle of sheet pan, for a total of 14 rolls. Spoon remaining enchilada sauce over the zucchini enchiladas and top with remaining cheese. Bake for 22-25 minutes, or until cheese is melted and filling is hot. Before serving, let enchiladas rest for 5-10 minutes so the rolls can absorb any excess moisture from the bottom of the pan. Serves 6

Nutritional Information 274 Calories, 13.9g Fat, 64.1mg Cholesterol, 662mg Sodium, 13.2g Carbohydrate, 25g Protein

Cinnamon-Toasted Oats

    2 teaspoons canola oil or olive oil
    1 teaspoon unsalted butter
    ½ cup rolled oats
    ¼ teaspoon cinnamon
    ⅛ teaspoon nutmeg
    1 teaspoon brown sugar

Heat oil and butter in a small nonstick skillet over medium-high heat. Add oats and stir to coat. Sprinkle with cinnamon and nutmeg; continue cooking and stirring until the oats are light golden brown, about 4 minutes.

Remove from heat; sprinkle with brown sugar and stir evenly to coat. Spread out on a plate to cool completely before serving or refrigerating in an airtight container for up to 4 days. Makes 1/2 cup. Serve with yogurt or fruit. Serves 1

Nutritional Information per 2 tablespoons: 60 Calories; protein 1.2g; 6g carbohydrates, fiber 1.1g, fat 4g; 2.5mg cholesterol

Melty Reuben

3 tablespoons light mayonnaise
2 tablespoons minced shallots
2 tablespoons minced dill pickles
1 tablespoon unsalted ketchup
1/2 teaspoon freshly ground black pepper
8 (3/4-ounce) slices rye bread
4 ounces thinly sliced lower-sodium roast beef
2 ounces thinly sliced lower-sodium corned beef
2 ounces Swiss cheese, shredded (about 1/2 cup)
2/3 cup kimchi, drained and thinly sliced Cooking spray

Combine first 5 ingredients in a small bowl, stirring well. Spread 1 1/2 table-spoons mayonnaise mixture over 1 side of each of 4 bread slices. Top each with 1 ounce roast beef, 1/2 ounce corned beef, and 2 tablespoons cheese. Top each sandwich with one-fourth of the kimchi and 1 bread slice.

Heat a large skillet over medium heat. Generously coat both sides of sandwiches with cooking spray. Arrange sandwiches in pan; cook 6 minutes or until lightly browned on both sides, turning once. Serves 4

Nutritional Information: 240 Calories; 7.2g Fat; 36mg Cholesterol; 799mg Sodium; 25g Carbohydrate; 3g Fiber; 18g Protein

Creamy Mushroom Chicken and Wild Rice Soup

2 tablespoons butter
1 pound mushrooms, sliced
1 tablespoon butter
1 onion, diced
2 carrots, diced
2 stalks celery, diced
2 cloves garlic, chopped
1 teaspoon thyme, chopped
6 cups chicken broth
1 cup wild rice (or a blend of rice including wild rice)
1 1/2 cups chicken, cooked and diced or shredded
1 cup fat-free half and half
1 cup Parmesan, grated
salt and pepper to taste

Melt the butter in a pan over medium-high heat, add the mushrooms and cook until the mushrooms have released their liquids and the liquid has evaporated, about 10-15 minutes, before setting aside. Melt the butter in the pan, add the onions, carrots and celery and cook until tender, about 8-10 minutes. Mix in the garlic and thyme and cook until fragrant, about a minute. Add the broth, rice, chicken and mushrooms, bring to a boil, reduce the heat and simmer, covered, until the rice is tender, about 20-30 minutes. Mix in the milk and cheese and cook until the cheese has melted, before seasoning with salt and pepper to taste. Serves 6

Nutritional Information: 443 Calories; 12g Fat; 65mg Cholesterol; 676mg Sodium; 38g Carbohydrates; 3g Fiber; 27g Protein

Peach Toast with Honey

6 thick slices brioche toasted
3 tablespoons whipped cream cheese
2 very ripe peaches, sliced 1/4" thick
Honey or maple syrup, for drizzling

Spread each toast evenly with whipped cream cheese or whipped butter and layer peaches on top. Drizzle with honey or maple syrup. Serves 6

Nutritional Information: 253 calories; 11.6 g total fat; 50 mg cholesterol; 220 mg sodium; 33.9 g carbohydrates; 2.2 g fiber; 5 g protein

Tuna Panini

3 tablespoons finely chopped red onion
3 tablespoons light mayonnaise
1 teaspoon grated lemon rind
1/4 teaspoon fennel seeds, crushed
1/4 teaspoon freshly ground black pepper
3 slices center-cut bacon, cooked and crumbled
2 (5-ounce) cans albacore tuna in water, drained and flaked
8 slices sourdough bread
(1/2-ounce) slices provolone cheese
Cooking spray

Combine first 7 ingredients in a medium bowl, stirring well to coat. Place 4 bread slices on a flat surface; top each bread slice with 1 cheese slice. Divide tuna mixture evenly among bread slices; top each serving with 1 remaining bread slice.

Heat a large skillet over medium heat. Lightly coat sandwiches with cooking spray. Place sandwiches in pan; top with another heavy skillet. Cook 3 minutes on each side or until lightly browned (leave skillet on sandwiches as they cook). Serves 4

Nutritional Information: 379 Calories; 12g Fat; 49mg Cholesterol; 33.3g Carbohydrate; 2.3g Fiber; 872mg Sodium; 6.9g Protein

Southwestern Steak Salad

1 pound flank steak, trimmed
11/2 teaspoons ground cumin
3/4 teaspoon salt, divided
1/4 teaspoon freshly ground pepper
6 tablespoons reduced-fat sour cream
2 tablespoons extra-virgin olive oil
2 tablespoons white vinegar
1-2 tablespoons minced chipotle peppers in adobo sauce
6 cups sliced romaine lettuce
11/2 cups corn kernels, fresh or frozen
1 firm ripe avocado, diced
2 medium tomatoes, cut into wedges
1/2 cup shredded Mexican cheese blend

Position oven rack about 3 inches from heat source; preheat broiler to high. Coat a broiler-safe pan with cooking spray. Sprinkle steak with cumin, 1/2 teaspoon salt and pepper. Place on the prepared pan and broil, turning once, until an instant-read thermometer inserted in the thickest part registers 125 degrees -130 degrees for medium-rare, 3 to 6 minutes per side. Let rest for 5 minutes. Thinly slice across the grain, then chop into bite-size pieces.

Meanwhile, whisk sour cream, oil, vinegar, chipotles to taste and the remaining 1/4 teaspoon salt in a large bowl. Transfer 4 tablespoons of the dressing to a small bowl. Add romaine, corn and avocado to the large bowl; toss to coat. Divide the salad and tomato wedges among 4 plates. Top each with cheese, the chopped steak and 1 tablespoon of the reserved dressing. Serves 4

Nutritional Information: 426 calories; 19.5 g total fat; 92 mg cholesterol; 604 mg sodium; 20.3 g carbohydrates; 7 g fiber; 32.6 g protein;

Apple Cinnamon Oatmeal

3 apples (about 3 cups), diced
2 tablespoons water
1 tablespoon butter
1 tablespoon maple syrup
½ teaspoon ground cinnamon
A pinch of sea salt
A drop of pure vanilla extract
2 cups prepared oatmeal

Put diced apple into a large skillet with 2 tablespoons water. Cover the skillet and cook over medium heat for about 5 minutes, stirring occasionally, until the apples become slightly soft.

Add 1 tablespoon butter to skillet. Stir apples and butter together until the apples are well coated. Cook for 5 minutes, stirring, occasionally, until the apples become soft.

Add Maple syrup, cinnamon, salt, and vanilla to the apples, and stir until well mixed. Cook for 5 minutes more, stirring constantly.

In the meantime, prepare oatmeal. Divide into separate bowls and top with caramelized apples, a good drizzle of the cooking juices, and a sprinkle of cinnamon. Serve immediately. Serves 4

Nutritional Information: 236 Calories; 11g Fat; 7g Protein; 31g Carbohydrate; 2g Fiber

Lemon Chicken Salad

4 cups water
2 bay leaves
9 ounces skinless, boneless chicken breast
1/4 cup plain 2% reduced-fat Greek yogurt
1 tablespoon olive oil
1 1/2 teaspoons fresh thyme leaves
1 teaspoon grated lemon rind
1/4 teaspoon kosher salt
1/4 teaspoon black pepper
2 tablespoons slivered red onion

Bring 4 cups water and bay leaves to a simmer in a saucepan. Add chicken; simmer 15 minutes or until done. Drain; discard bay leaves. Cool chicken slightly; shred. Serves 2

Combine yogurt, oil, thyme, rind, salt, and pepper in a medium bowl, stirring with a whisk. Add chicken and onion; toss well to combine.

Nutritional Information: 236 Calories; 11g Fat; 7g Protein; 31g Carbohydrate; 2g Fiber

Turkey Meatballs & Zucchini Noodles

1 pound ground turkey
1/4 cup seasoned dry breadcrumbs
1 large egg
3 tbsp. chopped fresh flat-leaf parsley
1/3 cup Parmesan cheese, grated, plus more for serving
2 garlic cloves, chopped, divided
Kosher salt
Freshly ground black pepper
2 tbsp. extra-virgin olive oil, divided
1 (25-oz.) jar marinara sauce
4 medium zucchini, cut into noodles with a spiralizer or julienne peeler
4 oz. Provolone cheese, grated

Combine turkey, breadcrumbs, egg, parsley, Parmesan, 1 garlic clove, and 1/2 teaspoon each salt and pepper in a bowl. Form into 12 meatballs. Heat 1 tablespoon oil in a large skillet over medium heat. Add meatballs and cook, turning occasionally, until brown on all sides, 4 to 6 minutes. Reduce heat to medium-low and gently stir in marinara. Simmer, turning meatballs occasionally, until meatballs are cooked through and sauce is thickened, 14 to 16 minutes. Meanwhile, heat remaining tablespoon oil in a medium skillet over medium-high heat. Add zucchini and remaining garlic and cook until just tender and heated through, 2 to 3 minutes. Season with salt and pepper.

Heat broiler to high with rack in the top position. Sprinkle provolone over meatballs. Broil until cheese is golden brown, 3 to 4 minutes. Serve meatballs over noodles topped with Parmesan. Serves 4

Nutritional Information: 526 Calories; 24g Fat; 27g Carbohydrate; 154mg Cholesterol; 6g Fiber; ; 1311mg Sodium

STEPS FOR SPIRITUAL GROWTH

—— GOD'S WORD FOR YOUR LIFE

I have hidden your word in my heart that I might not sin against you.

Psalm 119:11

As you begin to make decisions based on what God's Word teaches you, you will want to memorize what He has promised to those who trust and follow Him. Second Peter 1:3 tells us that God "has given us everything we need for life and godliness through our knowledge of him" (emphasis added). The Bible provides instruction and encouragement for any area of life in which you may be struggling. If you are dealing with a particular emotion or traumatic life event—fear, discouragement, stress, financial upset, the death of a loved one, a relationship difficulty—you can search through a Bible concordance for Scripture passages that deal with that particular situation. Scripture provides great comfort to those who memorize it.

One of the promises of knowing and obeying God's Word is that it gives you wisdom, insight, and understanding above all worldly knowledge (see Psalm 119:97–104). Psalm 119:129–130 says, "Your statutes are wonderful; therefore I obey them. The unfolding of your words gives light; it gives understanding to the simple." Now that's a precious promise about guidance for life!

The Value of Scripture Memory

Scripture memory is an important part of the Christian life. There are four key reasons to memorize Scripture:

1. **TO HANDLE DIFFICULT SITUATIONS.** A heartfelt knowledge of God's Word will equip you to handle any situation that you might face. Declaring such truth as, "I can do everything through Christ" (see Philippians 4:13) and "he will never leave me or forsake me" (see Hebrews 13:5) will enable you to walk through situations with peace and courage.

2. **TO OVERCOME TEMPTATION.** Luke 4:1–13 describes how Jesus used Scripture to overcome His temptations in the desert (see also Matthew 4:1-11). Knowledge of Scripture and the strength that comes with the ability to use it are important parts of putting on the full armor of God in preparation for spiritual warfare (see Ephesians 6:10–18).

3. **TO GET GUIDANCE.** Psalm 119:105 states the Word of God "is a lamp to my feet and a light for my path." You learn to hide God's Word in your heart so His light will direct your decisions and actions throughout your day.

4. **TO TRANSFORM YOUR MIND.** "Do not conform any longer to the pattern of this world, but be transformed by the renewing of your mind" (Romans 12:2). Scripture memory allows you to replace a lie with the truth of God's Word. When Scripture becomes firmly settled in your memory, not only will your thoughts connect with God's thoughts, but you will also be able to honor God with small everyday decisions as well as big life-impacting ones. Scripture memorization is the key to making a permanent lifestyle change in your thought patterns, which brings balance to every other area of your life.

Scripture Memory Tips

- Write the verse down, saying it aloud as you write it.
- Read verses before and after the memory verse to get its context.
- Read the verse several times, emphasizing a different word each time.
- Connect the Scripture reference to the first few words.
- Locate patterns, phrases, or keywords.
- Apply the Scripture to circumstances you are now experiencing.
- Pray the verse, making it personal to your life and inserting your name as the recipient of the promise or teaching. (Try that with 1 Corinthians 10:13, inserting "me" and "I" for "you.")
- Review the verse every day until it becomes second nature to think those words whenever your circumstances match its message. The Holy Spirit will bring the verse to mind when you need it most if you decide to plant it in your memory.

Scripture Memorization Made Easy!

What is your learning style? Do you learn by hearing, by sight, or by doing?

If you learn by hearing—if you are an auditory learner—singing the Scripture memory verses, reading them aloud, or recording them and listening to your recording will be very helpful in the memorization process.

If you are a visual learner, writing the verses and repeatedly reading through them will cement them in your mind.

If you learn by doing—if you are a tactile learner—creating motions for the words or using sign language will enable you to more easily recall the verse.

After determining your learning style, link your Scripture memory with a daily task, such as driving to work, walking on a treadmill, or eating lunch. Use these daily tasks as opportunities to memorize and review your verses.

Meals at home or out with friends can be used as a time to share the verse you are memorizing with those at your table. You could close your personal email messages by typing in your weekly memory verse. Or why not say your memory verse every time you brush your teeth or put on your shoes?

The purpose of Scripture memorization is to be able to apply God's words to your life. If you memorize Scripture using methods that connect with your particular learning style, you will find it easier to hide God's Word in your heart.

—— ESTABLISHING A QUIET TIME

Like all other components of the First Place for Health program, developing a live relationship with God is not a random act. You must intentionally seek God if you are to find Him! It's not that God plays hide-and-seek with you. He is always available to you. He invites you to come boldly into His presence. He reveals Himself to you in the pages of the Bible. And once you decide to earnestly seek Him, you are sure to find Him! When you delight in Him, your gracious God will give you the desires of your heart. Spending time getting to know God involves four basic elements: a priority, a plan, a place, and practice.

A Priority

You can successfully establish a quiet time with God by making this meeting a daily priority. This may require carving out time in your day so you have time and space for this new relationship you are cultivating. Often this will mean eliminating less important things so you will have time and space to meet with God. When speaking about Jesus, John the Baptist said, "He must become greater; I must become less" (John 3:30). You will undoubtedly find that to be true as well. What might you need to eliminate from your current schedule so that spending quality time with God can become a priority?

A Plan

Having made quiet time a priority, you will want to come up with a plan. This plan will include the time you have set aside to spend with God and a general outline of how you will spend your time in God's presence.

Elements you should consider incorporating into your quiet time include:

- Singing a song of praise
- Reading a daily selection in a devotional book or reading a psalm
- Using a systematic Scripture reading plan so you will be exposed to the whole truth of God's Word
- Completing your First Place for Health Bible study for that day
- Praying—silent, spoken, and written prayer
- Writing in your spiritual journal.

You will also want to make a list of the materials you will need to make your encounter with God more meaningful:

- A Bible
- Your First Place for Health Bible study
- Your prayer journal
- A pen and/or pencil
- A devotional book
- A Bible concordance
- A college-level dictionary
- A box of tissues (tears—both of sadness and joy—are often part of our quiet time with God!)

Think of how you would plan an important business meeting or social event, and then transfer that knowledge to your meeting time with God.

A Place

Having formulated a meeting-with-God plan, you will next need to create a meeting-with-God place. Of course, God is always with you; however, in order to have quality devotional time with Him, it is desirable that you find a comfortable meeting place. You will want to select a spot that is quiet and as distraction-free as possible. Meeting with God in the same place on a regular basis will help you remember what you are there for: to have an encounter with the true and living God!

Having selected the place, put the materials you have determined to use in your quiet time into a basket or on a nearby table or shelf. Now take the time to establish your personal quiet time with God. Tailor your quiet time to fit your needs—and the time you have allotted to spend with God. Although many people elect to meet with God early in the morning, for others afternoon or evening is best. There is no hard-and-fast rule about when your quiet time should be—the only essential thing is that you establish a quiet time!

Start with a small amount of time that you know you can devote yourself to daily. You can be confident that as you consistently spend time with God each day, the amount of time you can spend will increase as you are ready for the next level of your walk with God.

I will meet with God from _____ to _____ daily.

I plan to use that time with God to _____

_____

Supplies I will need to assemble include _____

_____

My meeting place with God will be _____

_____

Practice

After you have chosen the time and place to meet God each day and you have assembled your supplies, there are four easy steps for having a fruitful and worshipful time with the Lord.

STEP 1: Clear Your Heart and Mind

"Be still, and know that I am God" (Psalm 46:10). Begin your quiet time by reading the daily Bible selection from a devotional guide or a psalm. If you are new in your Christian walk, an excellent devotional guide to use is *Streams in the Desert* by L.B. Cowman. More mature Christians might benefit from My Utmost for His Highest by Oswald Chambers. Of course, you can use any devotional that has a strong emphasis on Scripture and prayer.

STEP 2: Read and Interact with Scripture

"I have hidden your word in my heart that I might not sin against you" (Psalm 119:11). As you open your Bible, ask the Holy Spirit to reveal something He knows you need for this day through the reading of His Word. Always try to find a nugget to encourage or direct you through the day. As you read the passage, pay special attention to the words and phrases the Holy Spirit brings to your attention. Some words may seem to resonate in your soul. You will want to spend time meditating on the passage, asking God what lesson He is teaching you.

After reading the Scripture passage over several times, ask yourself the following questions:

- In light of what I have read today, is there something I must now do? (Confess a sin? Claim a promise? Follow an example? Obey a command? Avoid a situation?)
- How should I respond to what I've read today?

STEP 3: Pray

"Be clear minded and self-controlled so that you can pray" (1 Peter 4:7). Spend time conversing with the Lord in prayer. Prayer is such an important part of First Place for Health that there is an entire section in this member's guide devoted to the practice of prayer.

STEP 4: Praise

"Praise the LORD, O my soul, and forget not all his benefits" (Psalm 103:2). End your quiet time with a time of praise. Be sure to thank the Lord of heaven and warmth for choosing to spend time with you!

—— SHARING YOUR FAITH

Nothing is more effective in drawing someone to Jesus than sharing personal life experiences. People are more open to the good news of Jesus Christ when they see faith in action. Personal faith stories are simple and effective ways to share what Christ is doing in your life, because they show firsthand how Christ makes a difference.

Sharing your faith story has an added benefit: it builds you up in your faith, too! Is your experience in First Place for Health providing you opportunities to share with others what God is doing in your life? If you answered yes, then you have a personal faith story!

If you do not have a personal faith story, perhaps it is because you don't know Jesus Christ as your personal Lord and Savior. Read through "Steps to Becoming a Christian" (which is the next chapter) and begin today to give Christ first place in your life.

Creativity and preparation in using opportunities to share a word or story about Jesus is an important part of the Christian life. Is Jesus helping you in a special way? Are you achieving a level of success or peace that you haven't experienced in other attempts to lose weight, exercise regularly, or eat healthier? As people see you making changes and achieving success, they may ask you how you are doing it. How will—or do—you respond? Remember, your story is unique, and it may allow others to see what Christ is doing in your life. It may also help to bring Christ into the life of another person.

Personal Statements of Faith

First Place for Health gives you a great opportunity to communicate your faith and express what God is doing in your life. Be ready to use your own personal statement of faith whenever the opportunity presents itself. Personal statements of faith should be short and fit naturally into a conversation. They don't require or expect any action or response from the listener. The goal is not to get another person to change but simply to help you communicate who you are and what's important to you.

Here are some examples of short statements of faith that you might use when someone asks what you are doing to lose weight:

- "I've been meeting with a group at my church. We pray together, support each other, learn about nutrition, and study the Bible."
- "It's amazing how Bible study and prayer are helping me lose weight and eat healthier."
- "I've had a lot of support from a group I meet with at church."
- "I'm relying more on God to help me make changes in my lifestyle."

Begin keeping a list of your meaningful experiences as you go through the First Place for Health program. Also notice what is happening in the lives of others. Use the following questions to help you prepare short personal statements and stories of faith:

- What is God doing in your life physically, mentally, emotionally, and spiritually?
- How has your relationship with God changed? Is it more intimate or personal?
- How is prayer, Bible study, and/or the support of others helping you achieve your goals for a healthy weight and good nutrition?

Writing Your Personal Faith Story

Write a brief story about how God is working in your life through First Place for Health. Use your story to help you share with others what's happening in your life.

Use the following questions to help develop your story:

- Why did you join First Place for Health? What specific circumstances led you to a Christ-centered health and weight-loss program? What were you feeling when you joined?
- What was your relationship with Christ when you started First Place for Health? What is it now?
- Has your experience in First Place for Health changed your relationship with Christ? With yourself? With others?
- How has your relationship with Christ, prayer, Bible study, and group support made a difference in your life?
- What specific verse or passage of Scripture has made a difference in the way you view yourself or your relationship with Christ?
- What experiences have impacted your life since starting First Place for Health?
- In what ways is Christ working in your life today? In what ways is He meeting your needs?
- How has Christ worked in other members of your First Place for Health group?

Answer the above questions in a few sentences, and then use your answers to help you write your own short personal faith story.

MEMBER SURVEY

We would love to know more about you. Share this form with your leader.

Name _____ Birth date _____

Tell us about your family.

_____

_____

_____

_____

Would you like to receive more information   Yes   No
about our church?

What area of expertise would you be willing to share with our class?

_____

_____

Why did you join First Place for Health?

_____

_____

With notice, would you be willing to lead a Bible study   Yes   No
discussion one week?

Are you comfortable praying out loud?   _____

Would you be willing to assist recording weights and/or   Yes   No
evaluating the Live It Trackers?

Any other comments:

_____

_____

PERSONAL WEIGHT AND MEASUREMENT RECORD

WEEK	WEIGHT	+ OR -	GOAL THIS SESSION	POUNDS TO GOAL
1				
2				
3				
4				
5				
6				
7				
8				
9				
10				
11				
12				

BEGINNING MEASUREMENTS

WAIST_____ HIPS_____ THIGHS_____ CHEST_____

ENDING MEASUREMENTS

WAIST_____ HIPS_____ THIGHS_____ CHEST_____

He has saved us and called us to a holy life — not because of anything we have done but because of His own purpose and grace. This grace was given us in Christ Jesus before the beginning of time. 2 Timothy 1:9

Date: _____

Name: _____

Home Phone: _____

Cell Phone: _____

Email: _____

Personal Prayer Concerns

_____

_____

_____

_____

_____

_____

_____

This form is for prayer requests that are personal to you and your journey in First Place for Health. Please complete and have it ready to turn in when you arrive at your group meeting.

*My flesh and my heart may fail, but God is the strength of my heart
and my portion forever. Psalm 73:26*

Date: _____

Name: _____

Home Phone: _____

Cell Phone: _____

Email: _____

Personal Prayer Concerns

_____

_____

_____

_____

_____

_____

_____

This form is for prayer requests that are personal to you and your journey in First Place for Health.
Please complete and have it ready to turn in when you arrive at your group meeting.

Then he said to them all: 'Whoever wants to be my disciple must deny themselves and take up their cross daily and follow me. For whoever wants to save their life will lose it, but whoever loses their life for me will save it.
Luke 9:23-24

Date: _____

Name: _____

Home Phone: _____

Cell Phone: _____

Email: _____

Personal Prayer Concerns

_____

_____

_____

_____

_____

_____

_____

This form is for prayer requests that are personal to you and your journey in First Place for Health. Please complete and have it ready to turn in when you arrive at your group meeting.

*And God is able to bless you abundantly, so that in all things at all
times, having all that you need, you will abound in every good work.*
2 Corinthians 9:8

Date: _____

Name: _____

Home Phone: _____

Cell Phone: _____

Email: _____

Personal Prayer Concerns

_____

_____

_____

_____

_____

_____

_____

This form is for prayer requests that are personal to you and your journey in First Place for Health.
Please complete and have it ready to turn in when you arrive at your group meeting.

Therefore everyone who hears these words of mine and puts them into practice is like a wise man who built his house on the rock. Matthew 7:24

Date: _____

Name: _____

Home Phone: _____

Cell Phone: _____

Email: _____

Personal Prayer Concerns

_____

_____

_____

_____

_____

_____

_____

This form is for prayer requests that are personal to you and your journey in First Place for Health. Please complete and have it ready to turn in when you arrive at your group meeting.

PRAYER PARTNER   **WEEK 6**

I have chosen the way of faithfulness; I have set my heart on your laws.
Psalm 119:30

Date: _____

Name: _____

Home Phone: _____

Cell Phone: _____

Email: _____

Personal Prayer Concerns

_____

_____

_____

_____

_____

_____

_____

This form is for prayer requests that are personal to you and your journey in First Place for Health. Please complete and have it ready to turn in when you arrive at your group meeting.

Direct my footsteps according to your word; let no sin rule over me.
Psalm 119:133

Date: _____

Name: _____

Home Phone: _____

Cell Phone: _____

Email: _____

Personal Prayer Concerns

_____

_____

_____

_____

_____

_____

_____

_____

This form is for prayer requests that are personal to you and your journey in First Place for Health. Please complete and have it ready to turn in when you arrive at your group meeting.

The LORD himself goes before you and will be with you; he will never leave you nor forsake you.
Do not be afraid; do not be discouraged.
Deuteronomy 31:8

Date: _____

Name: _____

Home Phone: _____

Cell Phone: _____

Email: _____

Personal Prayer Concern

_____

_____

_____

_____

_____

_____

_____

This form is for prayer requests that are personal to you and your journey in First Place for Health. Please complete and have it ready to turn in when you arrive at your group meeting.

PRAYER PARTNER

The name of the LORD is a fortified tower; the righteous run to it and are safe.

Proverbs 18:10

Date: _____

Name: _____

Home Phone: _____

Cell Phone: _____

Email: _____

Personal Prayer Concerns

_____

_____

_____

_____

_____

_____

_____

This form is for prayer requests that are personal to you and your journey in First Place for Health. Please complete and have it ready to turn in when you arrive at your group meeting.

LIVE IT TRACKER

Name: _____

My activity goal for next week:
○ None   ○ <30 min/day   ○ 30-60 min/day

My food goal for next week: _____
_____

Date: _____ Week #: _____

loss /gain _____ Calorie Range: _____

My week at a glance:
○ Great   ○ So-so   ○ Not so great

Activity level:
○ None   ○ <30 min/day   ○ 30-60 min/day

RECOMMENDED DAILY AMOUNT OF FOOD FROM EACH GROUP

GROUP	DAILY CALORIES							
	1300-1400	1500-1600	1700-1800	1900-2000	2100-2200	2300-2400	2500-2600	2700-2800
Fruits	1.5 – 2 c.	1.5 – 2 c.	1.5 – 2 c.	2 – 2.5 c.	2 – 2.5 c.	2.5 – 3.5 c.	3.5 – 4.5 c.	3.5 – 4.5 c.
Vegetables	1.5 – 2 c.	2 – 2.5 c.	2.5 – 3 c.	2.5 – 3 c.	3 – 3.5 c.	3.5 – 4.5 c..	4.5 – 5 c.	4.5 – 5 c.
Grains	5 oz eq.	5-6 oz eq.	6-7 oz eq.	6-7 oz eq.	7-8 oz eq.	8-9 oz eq.	9-10 oz eq.	10-11 oz eq.
Dairy	2-3 c.	3 c.	3 c.	3 c.	3 c.	3 c.	3 c.	3 c.
Protein	4 oz eq.	5 oz eq.	5-5.5 oz eq.	5.5-6.5 oz eq.	6.5-7 oz eq.	7-7.5 oz eq.	7-7.5 oz eq.	7.5-8 oz eq.
Healthy Oils & Other Fats	4 tsp.	5 tsp.	5 tsp.	6 tsp.	6 tsp.	7 tsp.	8 tsp.	8 tsp.
Water & Super Beverages*	Women: 9 c. Men: 13 c.	Women: 9 c. Men: 13 c.	Women: 9 c. Men: 13 c.	Women: 9 c. Men: 13 c.	Women: 9 c. Men: 13 c.	Women: 9 c. Men: 13 c.	Women: 9 c. Men: 13 c.	Women: 9 c. Men: 13 c.

*May count up to 3 cups caffeinated tea or coffee toward goal

DAILY FOOD GROUP TRACKER

	GROUP	FRUITS	VEGETABLES	GRAINS	PROTEIN	DAIRY	HEALTHY OILS & OTHER FATS	WATER & SUPER BEVERAGES
1	Estimate Total							
2	Estimate Total							
3	Estimate Total							
4	Estimate Total							
5	Estimate Total							
6	Estimate Total							
7	Estimate Total							

FOOD CHOICES   DAY 1

Breakfast: _____
Lunch: _____
Dinner: _____
Snacks: _____

PHYSICAL ACTIVITY   steps/miles/minutes: _____
description: _____

SPIRITUAL ACTIVITY
description: _____

FOOD CHOICES　　　　　　　　DAY ❷

Breakfast: _____

Lunch: _____

Dinner: _____

Snacks: _____

PHYSICAL ACTIVITY　steps/miles/minutes: | SPIRITUAL ACTIVITY

description: _____ | description: _____

_____ | _____

FOOD CHOICES　　　　　　　　DAY ❸

Breakfast: _____

Lunch: _____

Dinner: _____

Snacks: _____

PHYSICAL ACTIVITY　steps/miles/minutes: | SPIRITUAL ACTIVITY

description: _____ | description: _____

_____ | _____

FOOD CHOICES　　　　　　　　DAY ❹

Breakfast: _____

Lunch: _____

Dinner: _____

Snacks: _____

PHYSICAL ACTIVITY　steps/miles/minutes: | SPIRITUAL ACTIVITY

description: _____ | description: _____

_____ | _____

FOOD CHOICES　　　　　　　　DAY ❺

Breakfast: _____

Lunch: _____

Dinner: _____

Snacks: _____

PHYSICAL ACTIVITY　steps/miles/minutes: | SPIRITUAL ACTIVITY

description: _____ | description: _____

_____ | _____

FOOD CHOICES　　　　　　　　DAY ❻

Breakfast: _____

Lunch: _____

Dinner: _____

Snacks: _____

PHYSICAL ACTIVITY　steps/miles/minutes: | SPIRITUAL ACTIVITY

description: _____ | description: _____

_____ | _____

FOOD CHOICES　　　　　　　　DAY ❼

Breakfast: _____

Lunch: _____

Dinner: _____

Snacks: _____

PHYSICAL ACTIVITY　steps/miles/minutes: | SPIRITUAL ACTIVITY

description: _____ | description: _____

_____ | _____

LIVE IT TRACKER

Name: _____

My activity goal for next week:
○ None   ○ <30 min/day   ○ 30-60 min/day

My food goal for next week: _____
_____

Date: _____ Week #: _____

loss /gain _____ Calorie Range: _____

My week at a glance:
○ Great   ○ So-so   ○ Not so great

Activity level:
○ None   ○ <30 min/day   ○ 30-60 min/day

RECOMMENDED DAILY AMOUNT OF FOOD FROM EACH GROUP

GROUP	DAILY CALORIES							
	1300-1400	1500-1600	1700-1800	1900-2000	2100-2200	2300-2400	2500-2600	2700-2800
Fruits	1.5 – 2 c.	1.5 – 2 c.	1.5 – 2 c.	2 – 2.5 c.	2 – 2.5 c.	2.5 – 3.5 c.	3.5 – 4.5 c.	3.5 – 4.5 c.
Vegetables	1.5 – 2 c.	2 – 2.5 c.	2.5 – 3 c.	2.5 – 3 c.	3 – 3.5 c.	3.5 – 4.5 c.	4.5 – 5 c.	4.5 – 5 c.
Grains	5 oz eq.	5-6 oz eq.	6-7 oz eq.	6-7 oz eq.	7-8 oz eq.	8-9 oz eq.	9-10 oz eq.	10-11 oz eq.
Dairy	2-3 c.	3 c.	3 c.	3 c.	3 c.	3 c.	3 c.	3 c.
Protein	4 oz eq.	5 oz eq.	5-5.5 oz eq.	5.5-6.5 oz eq.	6.5-7 oz eq.	7-7.5 oz eq.	7-7.5 oz eq.	7.5-8 oz eq.
Healthy Oils & Other Fats	4 tsp.	5 tsp.	5 tsp.	6 tsp.	6 tsp.	7 tsp.	8 tsp.	8 tsp.
Water & Super Beverages*	Women: 9 c. Men: 13 c.	Women: 9 c. Men: 13 c.	Women: 9 c. Men: 13 c.	Women: 9 c. Men: 13 c.	Women: 9 c. Men: 13 c.	Women: 9 c. Men: 13 c.	Women: 9 c. Men: 13 c.	Women: 9 c. Men: 13 c.

*May count up to 3 cups caffeinated tea or coffee toward goal

DAILY FOOD GROUP TRACKER

	GROUP	FRUITS	VEGETABLES	GRAINS	PROTEIN	DAIRY	HEALTHY OILS & OTHER FATS	WATER & SUPER BEVERAGES
1	Estimate Total							
2	Estimate Total							
3	Estimate Total							
4	Estimate Total							
5	Estimate Total							
6	Estimate Total							
7	Estimate Total							

FOOD CHOICES   DAY ❶

Breakfast: _____
Lunch: _____
Dinner: _____
Snacks: _____

PHYSICAL ACTIVITY   steps/miles/minutes: _____

description: _____

SPIRITUAL ACTIVITY

description: _____

FOOD CHOICES DAY ❷

Breakfast: _____
Lunch: _____
Dinner: _____
Snacks: _____

PHYSICAL ACTIVITY   steps/miles/minutes: _____   SPIRITUAL ACTIVITY

description: _____   description: _____
_____   _____

FOOD CHOICES DAY ❸

Breakfast: _____
Lunch: _____
Dinner: _____
Snacks: _____

PHYSICAL ACTIVITY   steps/miles/minutes: _____   SPIRITUAL ACTIVITY

description: _____   description: _____
_____   _____

FOOD CHOICES DAY ❹

Breakfast: _____
Lunch: _____
Dinner: _____
Snacks: _____

PHYSICAL ACTIVITY   steps/miles/minutes: _____   SPIRITUAL ACTIVITY

description: _____   description: _____
_____   _____

FOOD CHOICES DAY ❺

Breakfast: _____
Lunch: _____
Dinner: _____
Snacks: _____

PHYSICAL ACTIVITY   steps/miles/minutes: _____   SPIRITUAL ACTIVITY

description: _____   description: _____
_____   _____

FOOD CHOICES DAY ❻

Breakfast: _____
Lunch: _____
Dinner: _____
Snacks: _____

PHYSICAL ACTIVITY   steps/miles/minutes: _____   SPIRITUAL ACTIVITY

description: _____   description: _____
_____   _____

FOOD CHOICES DAY ❼

Breakfast: _____
Lunch: _____
Dinner: _____
Snacks: _____

PHYSICAL ACTIVITY   steps/miles/minutes: _____   SPIRITUAL ACTIVITY

description: _____   description: _____
_____   _____

LIVE IT TRACKER

Name: _____

My activity goal for next week:
○ None   ○ <30 min/day   ○ 30-60 min/day

My food goal for next week: _____

Date: _____ Week #: _____

loss / gain _____ Calorie Range: _____

My week at a glance:
○ Great   ○ So-so   ○ Not so great

Activity level:
○ None   ○ <30 min/day   ○ 30-60 min/day

RECOMMENDED DAILY AMOUNT OF FOOD FROM EACH GROUP

GROUP	DAILY CALORIES							
	1300-1400	1500-1600	1700-1800	1900-2000	2100-2200	2300-2400	2500-2600	2700-2800
Fruits	1.5 – 2 c.	1.5 – 2 c.	1.5 – 2 c.	2 – 2.5 c.	2 – 2.5 c.	2.5 – 3.5 c.	3.5 – 4.5 c.	3.5 – 4.5 c.
Vegetables	1.5 – 2 c.	2 – 2.5 c.	2.5 – 3 c.	2.5 – 3 c.	3 – 3.5 c.	3.5 – 4.5 c.	4.5 – 5 c.	4.5 – 5 c.
Grains	5 oz eq.	5-6 oz eq.	6-7 oz eq.	6-7 oz eq.	7-8 oz eq.	8-9 oz eq.	9-10 oz eq.	10-11 oz eq.
Dairy	2-3 c.	3 c.	3 c.	3 c.	3 c.	3 c.	3 c.	3 c.
Protein	4 oz eq.	5 oz eq.	5-5.5 oz eq.	5.5-6.5 oz eq.	6.5-7 oz eq.	7-7.5 oz eq.	7-7.5 oz eq.	7.5-8 oz eq.
Healthy Oils & Other Fats	4 tsp.	5 tsp.	5 tsp.	6 tsp.	6 tsp.	7 tsp.	8 tsp.	8 tsp.
Water & Super Beverages*	Women: 9 c. Men: 13 c.	Women: 9 c. Men: 13 c.	Women: 9 c. Men: 13 c.	Women: 9 c. Men: 13 c.	Women: 9 c. Men: 13 c.	Women: 9 c. Men: 13 c.	Women: 9 c. Men: 13 c.	Women: 9 c. Men: 13 c.

*May count up to 3 cups caffeinated tea or coffee toward goal

DAILY FOOD GROUP TRACKER

	GROUP	FRUITS	VEGETABLES	GRAINS	PROTEIN	DAIRY	HEALTHY OILS & OTHER FATS	WATER & SUPER BEVERAGES
1	Estimate Total							
2	Estimate Total							
3	Estimate Total							
4	Estimate Total							
5	Estimate Total							
6	Estimate Total							
7	Estimate Total							

FOOD CHOICES

DAY 1

Breakfast: _____
Lunch: _____
Dinner: _____
Snacks: _____

PHYSICAL ACTIVITY   steps/miles/minutes: _____

description: _____

SPIRITUAL ACTIVITY

description: _____

FOOD CHOICES
DAY 2
Breakfast: _____
Lunch: _____
Dinner: _____
Snacks: _____

PHYSICAL ACTIVITY   steps/miles/minutes: _____
description: _____

SPIRITUAL ACTIVITY
description: _____

FOOD CHOICES
DAY 3
Breakfast: _____
Lunch: _____
Dinner: _____
Snacks: _____

PHYSICAL ACTIVITY   steps/miles/minutes: _____
description: _____

SPIRITUAL ACTIVITY
description: _____

FOOD CHOICES
DAY 4
Breakfast: _____
Lunch: _____
Dinner: _____
Snacks: _____

PHYSICAL ACTIVITY   steps/miles/minutes: _____
description: _____

SPIRITUAL ACTIVITY
description: _____

FOOD CHOICES
DAY 5
Breakfast: _____
Lunch: _____
Dinner: _____
Snacks: _____

PHYSICAL ACTIVITY   steps/miles/minutes: _____
description: _____

SPIRITUAL ACTIVITY
description: _____

FOOD CHOICES
DAY 6
Breakfast: _____
Lunch: _____
Dinner: _____
Snacks: _____

PHYSICAL ACTIVITY   steps/miles/minutes: _____
description: _____

SPIRITUAL ACTIVITY
description: _____

FOOD CHOICES
DAY 7
Breakfast: _____
Lunch: _____
Dinner: _____
Snacks: _____

PHYSICAL ACTIVITY   steps/miles/minutes: _____
description: _____

SPIRITUAL ACTIVITY
description: _____

LIVE IT TRACKER

Name: _____

Date: _____ Week #: _____

My activity goal for next week:
○ None ○ <30 min/day ○ 30-60 min/day

loss /gain _____ Calorie Range: _____

My food goal for next week: _____
_____

My week at a glance:
○ Great ○ So-so ○ Not so great

Activity level:
○ None ○ <30 min/day ○ 30-60 min/day

RECOMMENDED DAILY AMOUNT OF FOOD FROM EACH GROUP

GROUP	DAILY CALORIES							
	1300-1400	1500-1600	1700-1800	1900-2000	2100-2200	2300-2400	2500-2600	2700-2800
Fruits	1.5 – 2 c.	1.5 – 2 c.	1.5 – 2 c.	2 – 2.5 c.	2 – 2.5 c.	2.5 – 3.5 c.	3.5 – 4.5 c.	3.5 – 4.5 c.
Vegetables	1.5 – 2 c.	2 – 2.5 c.	2.5 – 3 c.	2.5 – 3 c.	3 – 3.5 c.	3.5 – 4.5 c.	4.5 – 5 c.	4.5 – 5 c.
Grains	5 oz eq.	5-6 oz eq.	6-7 oz eq.	6-7 oz eq.	7-8 oz eq.	8-9 oz eq.	9-10 oz eq.	10-11 oz eq.
Dairy	2-3 c.	3 c.	3 c.	3 c.	3 c.	3 c.	3 c.	3 c.
Protein	4 oz eq.	5 oz eq.	5-5.5 oz eq.	5.5-6.5 oz eq.	6.5-7 oz eq.	7-7.5 oz eq.	7-7.5 oz eq.	7.5-8 oz eq.
Healthy Oils & Other Fats	4 tsp.	5 tsp.	5 tsp.	6 tsp.	6 tsp.	7 tsp.	8 tsp.	8 tsp.
Water & Super Beverages*	Women: 9 c. Men: 13 c.	Women: 9 c. Men: 13 c.	Women: 9 c. Men: 13 c.	Women: 9 c. Men: 13 c.	Women: 9 c. Men: 13 c.	Women: 9 c. Men: 13 c.	Women: 9 c. Men: 13 c.	Women: 9 c. Men: 13 c.

*May count up to 3 cups caffeinated tea or coffee toward goal

DAILY FOOD GROUP TRACKER

GROUP	FRUITS	VEGETABLES	GRAINS	PROTEIN	DAIRY	HEALTHY OILS & OTHER FATS	WATER & SUPER BEVERAGES
1 Estimate Total							
2 Estimate Total							
3 Estimate Total							
4 Estimate Total							
5 Estimate Total							
6 Estimate Total							
7 Estimate Total							

FOOD CHOICES   DAY ❶

Breakfast: _____
Lunch: _____
Dinner: _____
Snacks: _____

PHYSICAL ACTIVITY steps/miles/minutes: _____

description: _____

SPIRITUAL ACTIVITY

description: _____

FOOD CHOICES   DAY ❷

Breakfast: _____

Lunch: _____

Dinner: _____

Snacks: _____

PHYSICAL ACTIVITY   steps/miles/minutes: | SPIRITUAL ACTIVITY

description: _____ | description: _____

_____ | _____

FOOD CHOICES   DAY ❸

Breakfast: _____

Lunch: _____

Dinner: _____

Snacks: _____

PHYSICAL ACTIVITY   steps/miles/minutes: | SPIRITUAL ACTIVITY

description: _____ | description: _____

_____ | _____

FOOD CHOICES   DAY ❹

Breakfast: _____

Lunch: _____

Dinner: _____

Snacks: _____

PHYSICAL ACTIVITY   steps/miles/minutes: | SPIRITUAL ACTIVITY

description: _____ | description: _____

_____ | _____

FOOD CHOICES   DAY ❺

Breakfast: _____

Lunch: _____

Dinner: _____

Snacks: _____

PHYSICAL ACTIVITY   steps/miles/minutes: | SPIRITUAL ACTIVITY

description: _____ | description: _____

_____ | _____

FOOD CHOICES   DAY ❻

Breakfast: _____

Lunch: _____

Dinner: _____

Snacks: _____

PHYSICAL ACTIVITY   steps/miles/minutes: | SPIRITUAL ACTIVITY

description: _____ | description: _____

_____ | _____

FOOD CHOICES   DAY ❼

Breakfast: _____

Lunch: _____

Dinner: _____

Snacks: _____

PHYSICAL ACTIVITY   steps/miles/minutes: | SPIRITUAL ACTIVITY

description: _____ | description: _____

_____ | _____

LIVE IT TRACKER

Name: _____

My activity goal for next week:
○ None   ○ <30 min/day   ○ 30-60 min/day

My food goal for next week: _____
_____

Date: _____ Week #: _____

loss / gain _____ Calorie Range: _____

My week at a glance:
○ Great   ○ So-so   ○ Not so great

Activity level:
○ None   ○ <30 min/day   ○ 30-60 min/day

RECOMMENDED DAILY AMOUNT OF FOOD FROM EACH GROUP

GROUP	DAILY CALORIES							
	1300-1400	1500-1600	1700-1800	1900-2000	2100-2200	2300-2400	2500-2600	2700-2800
Fruits	1.5 – 2 c.	1.5 – 2 c.	1.5 – 2 c.	2 – 2.5 c.	2 – 2.5 c.	2.5 – 3.5 c.	3.5 – 4.5 c.	3.5 – 4.5 c.
Vegetables	1.5 – 2 c.	2 – 2.5 c.	2.5 – 3 c.	2.5 – 3 c.	3 – 3.5 c.	3.5 – 4.5 c.	4.5 – 5 c.	4.5 – 5 c.
Grains	5 oz eq.	5-6 oz eq.	6-7 oz eq.	6-7 oz eq.	7-8 oz eq.	8-9 oz eq.	9-10 oz eq.	10-11 oz eq.
Dairy	2-3 c.	3 c.	3 c.	3 c.	3 c.	3 c.	3 c.	3 c.
Protein	4 oz eq.	5 oz eq.	5-5.5 oz eq.	5.5-6.5 oz eq.	6.5-7 oz eq.	7-7.5 oz eq.	7-7.5 oz eq.	7.5-8 oz eq.
Healthy Oils & Other Fats	4 tsp.	5 tsp.	5 tsp.	6 tsp.	6 tsp.	7 tsp.	8 tsp.	8 tsp.
Water & Super Beverages*	Women: 9 c. Men: 13 c.	Women: 9 c. Men: 13 c.	Women: 9 c. Men: 13 c.	Women: 9 c. Men: 13 c.	Women: 9 c. Men: 13 c.	Women: 9 c. Men: 13 c.	Women: 9 c. Men: 13 c.	Women: 9 c. Men: 13 c.

*May count up to 3 cups caffeinated tea or coffee toward goal

DAILY FOOD GROUP TRACKER

GROUP	FRUITS	VEGETABLES	GRAINS	PROTEIN	DAIRY	HEALTHY OILS & OTHER FATS	WATER & SUPER BEVERAGES
1 Estimate Total							
2 Estimate Total							
3 Estimate Total							
4 Estimate Total							
5 Estimate Total							
6 Estimate Total							
7 Estimate Total							

FOOD CHOICES   DAY ❶

Breakfast: _____
Lunch: _____
Dinner: _____
Snacks: _____

PHYSICAL ACTIVITY   steps/miles/minutes: _____

description: _____
_____

SPIRITUAL ACTIVITY

description: _____
_____

FOOD CHOICES   DAY ❷

Breakfast: _____
Lunch: _____
Dinner: _____
Snacks: _____

PHYSICAL ACTIVITY   steps/miles/minutes: | SPIRITUAL ACTIVITY

description: _____ | description: _____
_____ | _____

FOOD CHOICES   DAY ❸

Breakfast: _____
Lunch: _____
Dinner: _____
Snacks: _____

PHYSICAL ACTIVITY   steps/miles/minutes: | SPIRITUAL ACTIVITY

description: _____ | description: _____
_____ | _____

FOOD CHOICES   DAY ❹

Breakfast: _____
Lunch: _____
Dinner: _____
Snacks: _____

PHYSICAL ACTIVITY   steps/miles/minutes: | SPIRITUAL ACTIVITY

description: _____ | description: _____
_____ | _____

FOOD CHOICES   DAY ❺

Breakfast: _____
Lunch: _____
Dinner: _____
Snacks: _____

PHYSICAL ACTIVITY   steps/miles/minutes: | SPIRITUAL ACTIVITY

description: _____ | description: _____
_____ | _____

FOOD CHOICES   DAY ❻

Breakfast: _____
Lunch: _____
Dinner: _____
Snacks: _____

PHYSICAL ACTIVITY   steps/miles/minutes: | SPIRITUAL ACTIVITY

description: _____ | description: _____
_____ | _____

FOOD CHOICES   DAY ❼

Breakfast: _____
Lunch: _____
Dinner: _____
Snacks: _____

PHYSICAL ACTIVITY   steps/miles/minutes: | SPIRITUAL ACTIVITY

description: _____ | description: _____
_____ | _____

Name: _____   Date: _____ Week #: _____

My activity goal for next week: loss /gain _____ Calorie Range: _____

○ None   ○ <30 min/day   ○ 30-60 min/day

My week at a glance:

○ Great   ○ So-so   ○ Not so great

My food goal for next week: _____

Activity level:

○ None   ○ <30 min/day   ○ 30-60 min/day

RECOMMENDED DAILY AMOUNT OF FOOD FROM EACH GROUP

GROUP	DAILY CALORIES							
	1300-1400	1500-1600	1700-1800	1900-2000	2100-2200	2300-2400	2500-2600	2700-2800
Fruits	1.5 – 2 c.	1.5 – 2 c.	1.5 – 2 c.	2 – 2.5 c.	2 – 2.5 c.	2.5 – 3.5 c.	3.5 – 4.5 c.	3.5 – 4.5 c.
Vegetables	1.5 – 2 c.	2 – 2.5 c.	2.5 – 3 c.	2.5 – 3 c.	3 – 3.5 c.	3.5 – 4.5 c.	4.5 – 5 c.	4.5 – 5 c.
Grains	5 oz eq.	5-6 oz eq.	6-7 oz eq.	6-7 oz eq.	7-8 oz eq.	8-9 oz eq.	9-10 oz eq.	10-11 oz eq.
Dairy	2-3 c.	3 c.	3 c.	3 c.	3 c.	3 c.	3 c.	3 c.
Protein	4 oz eq.	5 oz eq.	5-5.5 oz eq.	5.5-6.5 oz eq.	6.5-7 oz eq.	7-7.5 oz eq.	7-7.5 oz eq.	7.5-8 oz eq.
Healthy Oils & Other Fats	4 tsp.	5 tsp.	5 tsp.	6 tsp.	6 tsp.	7 tsp.	8 tsp.	8 tsp.
Water & Super Beverages*	Women: 9 c. Men: 13 c.	Women: 9 c. Men: 13 c.	Women: 9 c. Men: 13 c.	Women: 9 c. Men: 13 c.	Women: 9 c. Men: 13 c.	Women: 9 c. Men: 13 c.	Women: 9 c. Men: 13 c.	Women: 9 c. Men: 13 c.

*May count up to 3 cups caffeinated tea or coffee toward goal

DAILY FOOD GROUP TRACKER

GROUP	FRUITS	VEGETABLES	GRAINS	PROTEIN	DAIRY	HEALTHY OILS & OTHER FATS	WATER & SUPER BEVERAGES
1 Estimate Total							
2 Estimate Total							
3 Estimate Total							
4 Estimate Total							
5 Estimate Total							
6 Estimate Total							
7 Estimate Total							

FOOD CHOICES   DAY ❶

Breakfast: _____

Lunch: _____

Dinner: _____

Snacks: _____

PHYSICAL ACTIVITY   steps/miles/minutes: _____

description: _____

SPIRITUAL ACTIVITY

description: _____

FOOD CHOICES   DAY ❷

Breakfast: _____
Lunch: _____
Dinner: _____
Snacks: _____

PHYSICAL ACTIVITY steps/miles/minutes:	SPIRITUAL ACTIVITY
description: _____	description: _____
_____	_____

FOOD CHOICES   DAY ❸

Breakfast: _____
Lunch: _____
Dinner: _____
Snacks: _____

PHYSICAL ACTIVITY steps/miles/minutes:	SPIRITUAL ACTIVITY
description: _____	description: _____
_____	_____

FOOD CHOICES   DAY ❹

Breakfast: _____
Lunch: _____
Dinner: _____
Snacks: _____

PHYSICAL ACTIVITY steps/miles/minutes:	SPIRITUAL ACTIVITY
description: _____	description: _____
_____	_____

FOOD CHOICES   DAY ❺

Breakfast: _____
Lunch: _____
Dinner: _____
Snacks: _____

PHYSICAL ACTIVITY steps/miles/minutes:	SPIRITUAL ACTIVITY
description: _____	description: _____
_____	_____

FOOD CHOICES   DAY ❻

Breakfast: _____
Lunch: _____
Dinner: _____
Snacks: _____

PHYSICAL ACTIVITY steps/miles/minutes:	SPIRITUAL ACTIVITY
description: _____	description: _____
_____	_____

FOOD CHOICES   DAY ❼

Breakfast: _____
Lunch: _____
Dinner: _____
Snacks: _____

PHYSICAL ACTIVITY steps/miles/minutes:	SPIRITUAL ACTIVITY
description: _____	description: _____
_____	_____

LIVE IT TRACKER

Name: _____   Date: _____ Week #: _____

My activity goal for next week:
○ None   ○ <30 min/day   ○ 30-60 min/day

loss / gain _____ Calorie Range: _____

My week at a glance:
○ Great   ○ So-so   ○ Not so great

My food goal for next week: _____

Activity level:
○ None   ○ <30 min/day   ○ 30-60 min/day

RECOMMENDED DAILY AMOUNT OF FOOD FROM EACH GROUP

GROUP	DAILY CALORIES							
	1300-1400	1500-1600	1700-1800	1900-2000	2100-2200	2300-2400	2500-2600	2700-2800
Fruits	1.5 – 2 c.	1.5 – 2 c.	1.5 – 2 c.	2 – 2.5 c.	2 – 2.5 c.	2.5 – 3.5 c.	3.5 – 4.5 c.	3.5 – 4.5 c.
Vegetables	1.5 – 2 c.	2 – 2.5 c.	2.5 – 3 c.	2.5 – 3 c.	3 – 3.5 c.	3.5 – 4.5 c..	4.5 – 5 c.	4.5 – 5 c.
Grains	5 oz eq.	5-6 oz eq.	6-7 oz eq.	6-7 oz eq.	7-8 oz eq.	8-9 oz eq.	9-10 oz eq.	10-11 oz eq.
Dairy	2-3 c.	3 c.	3 c.	3 c.	3 c.	3 c.	3 c.	3 c.
Protein	4 oz eq.	5 oz eq.	5-5.5 oz eq.	5.5-6.5 oz eq.	6.5-7 oz eq.	7-7.5 oz eq.	7-7.5 oz eq.	7.5-8 oz eq.
Healthy Oils & Other Fats	4 tsp.	5 tsp.	5 tsp.	6 tsp.	6 tsp.	7 tsp.	8 tsp.	8 tsp.
Water & Super Beverages*	Women: 9 c. Men: 13 c.	Women: 9 c. Men: 13 c.	Women: 9 c. Men: 13 c.	Women: 9 c. Men: 13 c.	Women: 9 c. Men: 13 c.	Women: 9 c. Men: 13 c.	Women: 9 c. Men: 13 c.	Women: 9 c. Men: 13 c.

*May count up to 3 cups caffeinated tea or coffee toward goal

DAILY FOOD GROUP TRACKER

GROUP	FRUITS	VEGETABLES	GRAINS	PROTEIN	DAIRY	HEALTHY OILS & OTHER FATS	WATER & SUPER BEVERAGES
1 Estimate Total							
2 Estimate Total							
3 Estimate Total							
4 Estimate Total							
5 Estimate Total							
6 Estimate Total							
7 Estimate Total							

FOOD CHOICES   DAY ❶

Breakfast: _____
Lunch: _____
Dinner: _____
Snacks: _____

PHYSICAL ACTIVITY   steps/miles/minutes: _____

description: _____

SPIRITUAL ACTIVITY

description: _____

FOOD CHOICES   DAY ❷

Breakfast: _____
Lunch: _____
Dinner: _____
Snacks: _____

PHYSICAL ACTIVITY steps/miles/minutes:	SPIRITUAL ACTIVITY
description: _____	description: _____
_____	_____

FOOD CHOICES   DAY ❸

Breakfast: _____
Lunch: _____
Dinner: _____
Snacks: _____

PHYSICAL ACTIVITY steps/miles/minutes:	SPIRITUAL ACTIVITY
description: _____	description: _____
_____	_____

FOOD CHOICES   DAY ❹

Breakfast: _____
Lunch: _____
Dinner: _____
Snacks: _____

PHYSICAL ACTIVITY steps/miles/minutes:	SPIRITUAL ACTIVITY
description: _____	description: _____
_____	_____

FOOD CHOICES   DAY ❺

Breakfast: _____
Lunch: _____
Dinner: _____
Snacks: _____

PHYSICAL ACTIVITY steps/miles/minutes:	SPIRITUAL ACTIVITY
description: _____	description: _____
_____	_____

FOOD CHOICES   DAY ❻

Breakfast: _____
Lunch: _____
Dinner: _____
Snacks: _____

PHYSICAL ACTIVITY steps/miles/minutes:	SPIRITUAL ACTIVITY
description: _____	description: _____
_____	_____

FOOD CHOICES   DAY ❼

Breakfast: _____
Lunch: _____
Dinner: _____
Snacks: _____

PHYSICAL ACTIVITY steps/miles/minutes:	SPIRITUAL ACTIVITY
description: _____	description: _____
_____	_____

LIVE IT TRACKER

Name: _____

My activity goal for next week:
○ None　○ <30 min/day　○ 30-60 min/day

My food goal for next week: _____
_____

Date: _____ Week #: _____

loss / gain _____ Calorie Range: _____

My week at a glance:
○ Great　○ So-so　○ Not so great

Activity level:
○ None　○ <30 min/day　○ 30-60 min/day

RECOMMENDED DAILY AMOUNT OF FOOD FROM EACH GROUP

GROUP	DAILY CALORIES							
	1300-1400	1500-1600	1700-1800	1900-2000	2100-2200	2300-2400	2500-2600	2700-2800
Fruits	1.5 – 2 c.	1.5 – 2 c.	1.5 – 2 c.	2 – 2.5 c.	2 – 2.5 c.	2.5 – 3.5 c.	3.5 – 4.5 c.	3.5 – 4.5 c.
Vegetables	1.5 – 2 c.	2 – 2.5 c.	2.5 – 3 c.	2.5 – 3 c.	3 – 3.5 c.	3.5 – 4.5 c.	4.5 – 5 c.	4.5 – 5 c.
Grains	5 oz eq.	5-6 oz eq.	6-7 oz eq.	6-7 oz eq.	7-8 oz eq.	8-9 oz eq.	9-10 oz eq.	10-11 oz eq.
Dairy	2-3 c.	3 c.	3 c.	3 c.	3 c.	3 c.	3 c.	3 c.
Protein	4 oz eq.	5 oz eq.	5-5.5 oz eq.	5.5-6.5 oz eq.	6.5-7 oz eq.	7-7.5 oz eq.	7-7.5 oz eq.	7.5-8 oz eq.
Healthy Oils & Other Fats	4 tsp.	5 tsp.	5 tsp.	6 tsp.	6 tsp.	7 tsp.	8 tsp.	8 tsp.
Water & Super Beverages*	Women: 9 c. Men: 13 c.	Women: 9 c. Men: 13 c.	Women: 9 c. Men: 13 c.	Women: 9 c. Men: 13 c.	Women: 9 c. Men: 13 c.	Women: 9 c. Men: 13 c.	Women: 9 c. Men: 13 c.	Women: 9 c. Men: 13 c.

*May count up to 3 cups caffeinated tea or coffee toward goal

DAILY FOOD GROUP TRACKER

GROUP	FRUITS	VEGETABLES	GRAINS	PROTEIN	DAIRY	HEALTHY OILS & OTHER FATS	WATER & SUPER BEVERAGES
❶ Estimate Total							
❷ Estimate Total							
❸ Estimate Total							
❹ Estimate Total							
❺ Estimate Total							
❻ Estimate Total							
❼ Estimate Total							

FOOD CHOICES　　　　　　　　　　　　　　　　　　　　DAY ❶

Breakfast: _____
Lunch: _____
Dinner: _____
Snacks: _____

PHYSICAL ACTIVITY　steps/miles/minutes: _____

description: _____

SPIRITUAL ACTIVITY

description: _____

FOOD CHOICES   DAY ❷

Breakfast: _____

Lunch: _____

Dinner: _____

Snacks: _____

PHYSICAL ACTIVITY steps/miles/minutes:	SPIRITUAL ACTIVITY
description: _____	description: _____

FOOD CHOICES   DAY ❸

Breakfast: _____

Lunch: _____

Dinner: _____

Snacks: _____

PHYSICAL ACTIVITY steps/miles/minutes:	SPIRITUAL ACTIVITY
description: _____	description: _____

FOOD CHOICES   DAY ❹

Breakfast: _____

Lunch: _____

Dinner: _____

Snacks: _____

PHYSICAL ACTIVITY steps/miles/minutes:	SPIRITUAL ACTIVITY
description: _____	description: _____

FOOD CHOICES   DAY ❺

Breakfast: _____

Lunch: _____

Dinner: _____

Snacks: _____

PHYSICAL ACTIVITY steps/miles/minutes:	SPIRITUAL ACTIVITY
description: _____	description: _____

FOOD CHOICES   DAY ❻

Breakfast: _____

Lunch: _____

Dinner: _____

Snacks: _____

PHYSICAL ACTIVITY steps/miles/minutes:	SPIRITUAL ACTIVITY
description: _____	description: _____

FOOD CHOICES   DAY ❼

Breakfast: _____

Lunch: _____

Dinner: _____

Snacks: _____

PHYSICAL ACTIVITY steps/miles/minutes:	SPIRITUAL ACTIVITY
description: _____	description: _____

LIVE IT TRACKER

Name: _____

Date: _____ Week #: _____

My activity goal for next week:
○ None   ○ <30 min/day   ○ 30-60 min/day

loss/gain _____ Calorie Range: _____

My week at a glance:
○ Great   ○ So-so   ○ Not so great

My food goal for next week: _____

Activity level:
○ None ○ <30 min/day ○ 30-60 min/day

RECOMMENDED DAILY AMOUNT OF FOOD FROM EACH GROUP

GROUP	DAILY CALORIES							
	1300-1400	1500-1600	1700-1800	1900-2000	2100-2200	2300-2400	2500-2600	2700-2800
Fruits	1.5 – 2 c.	1.5 – 2 c.	1.5 – 2 c.	2 – 2.5 c.	2 – 2.5 c.	2.5 – 3.5 c.	3.5 – 4.5 c.	3.5 – 4.5 c.
Vegetables	1.5 – 2 c.	2 – 2.5 c.	2.5 – 3 c.	2.5 – 3 c.	3 – 3.5 c.	3.5 – 4.5 c.	4.5 – 5 c.	4.5 – 5 c.
Grains	5 oz eq.	5-6 oz eq.	6-7 oz eq.	6-7 oz eq.	7-8 oz eq.	8-9 oz eq.	9-10 oz eq.	10-11 oz eq.
Dairy	2-3 c.	3 c.	3 c.	3 c.	3 c.	3 c.	3 c.	3 c.
Protein	4 oz eq.	5 oz eq.	5-5.5 oz eq.	5.5-6.5 oz eq.	6.5-7 oz eq.	7-7.5 oz eq.	7-7.5 oz eq.	7.5-8 oz eq.
Healthy Oils & Other Fats	4 tsp.	5 tsp.	5 tsp.	6 tsp.	6 tsp.	7 tsp.	8 tsp.	8 tsp.
Water & Super Beverages*	Women: 9 c. Men: 13 c.	Women: 9 c. Men: 13 c.	Women: 9 c. Men: 13 c.	Women: 9 c. Men: 13 c.	Women: 9 c. Men: 13 c.	Women: 9 c. Men: 13 c.	Women: 9 c. Men: 13 c.	Women: 9 c. Men: 13 c.

*May count up to 3 cups caffeinated tea or coffee toward goal

DAILY FOOD GROUP TRACKER

GROUP	FRUITS	VEGETABLES	GRAINS	PROTEIN	DAIRY	HEALTHY OILS & OTHER FATS	WATER & SUPER BEVERAGES
1 Estimate Total							
2 Estimate Total							
3 Estimate Total							
4 Estimate Total							
5 Estimate Total							
6 Estimate Total							
7 Estimate Total							

FOOD CHOICES   DAY ❶

Breakfast: _____
Lunch: _____
Dinner: _____
Snacks: _____

PHYSICAL ACTIVITY   steps/miles/minutes: _____

description: _____

SPIRITUAL ACTIVITY

description: _____

FOOD CHOICES DAY 2

Breakfast: _____
Lunch: _____
Dinner: _____
Snacks: _____

PHYSICAL ACTIVITY   steps/miles/minutes: _____

description: _____

SPIRITUAL ACTIVITY

description: _____

FOOD CHOICES DAY 3

Breakfast: _____
Lunch: _____
Dinner: _____
Snacks: _____

PHYSICAL ACTIVITY   steps/miles/minutes: _____

description: _____

SPIRITUAL ACTIVITY

description: _____

FOOD CHOICES DAY 4

Breakfast: _____
Lunch: _____
Dinner: _____
Snacks: _____

PHYSICAL ACTIVITY   steps/miles/minutes: _____

description: _____

SPIRITUAL ACTIVITY

description: _____

FOOD CHOICES DAY 5

Breakfast: _____
Lunch: _____
Dinner: _____
Snacks: _____

PHYSICAL ACTIVITY   steps/miles/minutes: _____

description: _____

SPIRITUAL ACTIVITY

description: _____

FOOD CHOICES DAY 6

Breakfast: _____
Lunch: _____
Dinner: _____
Snacks: _____

PHYSICAL ACTIVITY   steps/miles/minutes: _____

description: _____

SPIRITUAL ACTIVITY

description: _____

FOOD CHOICES DAY 7

Breakfast: _____
Lunch: _____
Dinner: _____
Snacks: _____

PHYSICAL ACTIVITY   steps/miles/minutes: _____

description: _____

SPIRITUAL ACTIVITY

description: _____

LIVE IT TRACKER

Name: _____

Date: _____ Week #: _____

My activity goal for next week:
○ None   ○ <30 min/day   ○ 30-60 min/day

My food goal for next week: _____
_____

loss /gain _____ Calorie Range: _____

My week at a glance:
○ Great   ○ So-so   ○ Not so great

Activity level:
○ None   ○ <30 min/day   ○ 30-60 min/day

RECOMMENDED DAILY AMOUNT OF FOOD FROM EACH GROUP

GROUP	DAILY CALORIES							
....	1300-1400	1500-1600	1700-1800	1900-2000	2100-2200	2300-2400	2500-2600	2700-2800
Fruits	1.5 – 2 c.	1.5 – 2 c.	1.5 – 2 c.	2 – 2.5 c.	2 – 2.5 c.	2.5 – 3.5 c.	3.5 – 4.5 c.	3.5 – 4.5 c.
Vegetables	1.5 – 2 c.	2 – 2.5 c.	2.5 – 3 c.	2.5 – 3 c.	3 – 3.5 c.	3.5 – 4.5 c.	4.5 – 5 c.	4.5 – 5 c.
Grains	5 oz eq.	5-6 oz eq.	6-7 oz eq.	6-7 oz eq.	7-8 oz eq.	8-9 oz eq.	9-10 oz eq.	10-11 oz eq.
Dairy	2-3 c.	3 c.	3 c.	3 c.	3 c.	3 c.	3 c.	3 c.
Protein	4 oz eq.	5 oz eq.	5-5.5 oz eq.	5.5-6.5 oz eq.	6.5-7 oz eq.	7-7.5 oz eq.	7-7.5 oz eq.	7.5-8 oz eq.
Healthy Oils & Other Fats	4 tsp.	5 tsp.	5 tsp.	6 tsp.	6 tsp.	7 tsp.	8 tsp.	8 tsp.
Water & Super Beverages*	Women: 9 c. Men: 13 c.	Women: 9 c. Men: 13 c.	Women: 9 c. Men: 13 c.	Women: 9 c. Men: 13 c.	Women: 9 c. Men: 13 c.	Women: 9 c. Men: 13 c.	Women: 9 c. Men: 13 c.	Women: 9 c. Men: 13 c.

*May count up to 3 cups caffeinated tea or coffee toward goal

DAILY FOOD GROUP TRACKER

GROUP	FRUITS	VEGETABLES	GRAINS	PROTEIN	DAIRY	HEALTHY OILS & OTHER FATS	WATER & SUPER BEVERAGES
1 Estimate Total							
2 Estimate Total							
3 Estimate Total							
4 Estimate Total							
5 Estimate Total							
6 Estimate Total							
7 Estimate Total							

FOOD CHOICES   DAY ❶

Breakfast: _____
Lunch: _____
Dinner: _____
Snacks: _____

PHYSICAL ACTIVITY   steps/miles/minutes: _____

description: _____
_____

SPIRITUAL ACTIVITY

description: _____
_____

FOOD CHOICES

DAY ❷

Breakfast: _____

Lunch: _____

Dinner: _____

Snacks: _____

| PHYSICAL ACTIVITY | steps/miles/minutes: | SPIRITUAL ACTIVITY |

description: _____ | description: _____

FOOD CHOICES

DAY ❸

Breakfast: _____

Lunch: _____

Dinner: _____

Snacks: _____

| PHYSICAL ACTIVITY | steps/miles/minutes: | SPIRITUAL ACTIVITY |

description: _____ | description: _____

FOOD CHOICES

DAY ❹

Breakfast: _____

Lunch: _____

Dinner: _____

Snacks: _____

| PHYSICAL ACTIVITY | steps/miles/minutes: | SPIRITUAL ACTIVITY |

description: _____ | description: _____

FOOD CHOICES

DAY ❺

Breakfast: _____

Lunch: _____

Dinner: _____

Snacks: _____

| PHYSICAL ACTIVITY | steps/miles/minutes: | SPIRITUAL ACTIVITY |

description: _____ | description: _____

FOOD CHOICES

DAY ❻

Breakfast: _____

Lunch: _____

Dinner: _____

Snacks: _____

| PHYSICAL ACTIVITY | steps/miles/minutes: | SPIRITUAL ACTIVITY |

description: _____ | description: _____

FOOD CHOICES

DAY ❼

Breakfast: _____

Lunch: _____

Dinner: _____

Snacks: _____

| PHYSICAL ACTIVITY | steps/miles/minutes: | SPIRITUAL ACTIVITY |

description: _____ | description: _____

100-MILE CLUB

WALKING			
slowly, 2 mph	30 min =	156 cal =	1 mile
moderately, 3 mph	20 min =	156 cal =	1 mile
very briskly, 4 mph	15 min =	156 cal =	1 mile
speed walking	10 min =	156 cal =	1 mile
up stairs	13 min =	159 cal =	1 mile
RUNNING / JOGGING			
• • •	10 min =	156 cal =	1 mile
CYCLE OUTDOORS			
slowly, < 10 mph	20 min =	156 cal =	1 mile
light effort, 10-12 mph	12 min =	156 cal =	1 mile
moderate effort, 12-14 mph	10 min =	156 cal =	1 mile
vigorous effort, 14-16 mph	7.5 min =	156 cal =	1 mile
very fast, 16-19 mph	6.5 min =	152 cal =	1 mile
SPORTS ACTIVITIES			
playing tennis (singles)	10 min =	156 cal =	1 mile
swimming			
light to moderate effort	11 min =	152 cal =	1 mile
fast, vigorous effort	7.5 min =	156 cal =	1 mile
softball	15 min =	156 cal =	1 mile
golf	20 min =	156 cal =	1 mile
rollerblading	6.5 min =	152 cal =	1 mile
ice skating	11 min =	152 cal =	1 mile
jumping rope	7.5 min =	156 cal =	1 mile
basketball	12 min =	156 cal =	1 mile
soccer (casual)	15 min =	159 min =	1 mile
AROUND THE HOUSE			
mowing grass	22 min =	156 cal =	1 mile
mopping, sweeping, vacuuming	19.5 min =	155 cal =	1 mile
cooking	40 min =	160 cal =	1 mile
gardening	19 min =	156 cal =	1 mile
housework (general)	35 min =	156 cal =	1 mile

AROUND THE HOUSE			
ironing	45 min =	153 cal =	1 mile
raking leaves	25 min =	150 cal =	1 mile
washing car	23 min =	156 cal =	1 mile
washing dishes	45 min =	153 cal =	1 mile
AT THE GYM			
stair machine	8.5 min =	155 cal =	1 mile
stationary bike			
slowly, 10 mph	30 min =	156 cal =	1 mile
moderately, 10-13 mph	15 min =	156 cal =	1 mile
vigorously, 13-16 mph	7.5 min =	156 cal =	1 mile
briskly, 16-19 mph	6.5 min =	156 cal =	1 mile
elliptical trainer	12 min =	156 cal =	1 mile
weight machines (vigorously)	13 min =	152 cal =	1 mile
aerobics			
low impact	15 min =	156 cal =	1 mile
high impact	12 min =	156 cal =	1 mile
water	20 min =	156 cal =	1 mile
pilates	15 min =	156 cal =	1 mile
raquetball (casual)	15 min =	156 cal =	1 mile
stretching exercises	25 min =	150 cal =	1 mile
weight lifting (also works for weight machines used moderately or gently)	30 min =	156 cal =	1 mile
FAMILY LEISURE			
playing piano	37 min =	155 cal =	1 mile
jumping rope	10 min =	152 cal =	1 mile
skating (moderate)	20 min =	152 cal =	1 mile
swimming			
moderate	17 min =	156 cal =	1 mile
vigorous	10 min =	148 cal =	1 mile
table tennis	25 min =	150 cal =	1 mile
walk / run / play with kids	25 min =	150 cal =	1 mile

Let's Count Our Miles!

Color each circle to represent a mile you've completed.
Watch your progress to that 100 mile marker!

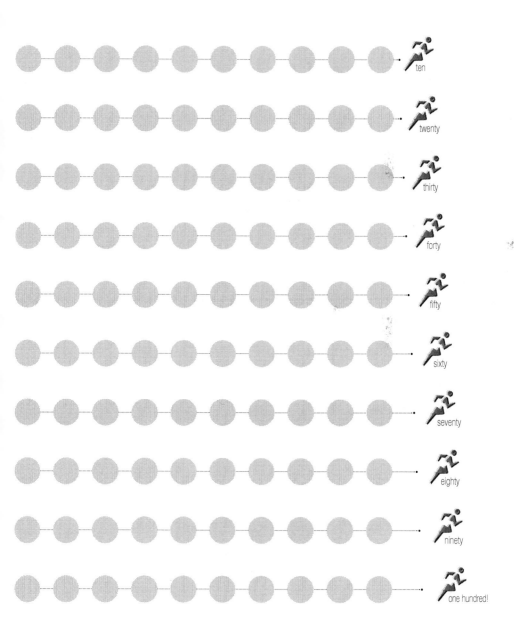

ten

twenty

thirty

forty

fifty

sixty

seventy

eighty

ninety

one hundred!

Made in the USA
Columbia, SC
31 January 2023

11369977R00126